THE FIRST TIME FATHER 2-IN 1 VALUE BUNDLE

THE FIRST TIME DAD'S GUIDE FROM PREGNANCY TO TODDLER

ALFIE THOMAS

CONTENTS

FIRST TIME FATHER' BABY'S FIRST YEAR
The Ultimate First Time Dads' Guide from Baby to Toddler

BOOK DESCRIPTION

It's a beautiful and exciting time for the entire family. You are about to enter into an amazing journey of fatherhood, but first, you need to prepare yourself mentally and physically. This 134-page boo, "THE FIRST FATHER: The Expectant Survival Guide For First-time Dads Through pregnancy Journey" is here to help you step by step in every aspect of your life as a dad-to-be.

It is a comprehensive guide to all the aspects of parenting for both expectant dads and first-time fathers. It covers every aspect related to pregnancy, childbirth, and early childhood roles in a simple language that can be understood by anyone.

Fun Fact:

The First Father: The Expectant Survival Guide For First-Time Dads Through Pregnancy Journey focuses on helping first-time expectant fathers to understand what they are going through and how to make the best of it. The book has been written out of my personal experience as well as experiences shared by other fathers. It is safe to say that this book will help you to make decisions on your own without any kind of confusion or doubt.

The book is divided into three parts. The first part talks about pregnancy and how you can support your pregnant partner during pregnancy. We called it the pregnancy superstar because you will become a champion by the time your little one is born. The second part discusses father-child bonding through special skills, such as diaper-changing guides, feeding, and bathing your newborn. Did we leave out other special tips, such as the new dad survival kit and cheatsheet? Of course not! You are covered in all angles of surviving fatherhood. The final part focused on how you can take care of your mental health, get your finances in order, and the general rules of child upbringing.

SOME HEADLINES IN THE BOOK:

- The story of How I Became a Father

PART 1:

- The Pregnancy Superstar
- Basic Knowledge Of Pregnancy
- Prepare Now Or Pay Later
- Getting Your **S Ready
- Helping Mommy To Save The Baby
- Your Partner's Mind Exposed!

- The P's And Q's Of Pregnancy
- Some Sex Positions You Could Try
- Things To Avoid (The Don'ts Of Pregnancy)
- The New Dad Cheatsheet
- Transition With Baby From Hospital To Home

PART 2:

- New Dad Survival Kit
- Baby Registry - Must-Have Items
- Designing A Baby Nursery In 4 Steps
- Playmate - Growing A Bond
- How To Feed Your Tot
- Bathing And Dressing A Newborn
- Becoming A Diaper-Changing Machine
- Nightime – Skeleton In The Cupboard

PART 3:

- The New Dad Mindset
- How To Defeat The Fubb In You
- Managing Your Finances
- Coaching Your Child.

You're one click away from unlocking your best father-hood potential...

ACKNOWLEDGMENTS

I'd like to thank Mirabelle, my pregnant wife/best friend/inspiration/partner/editor/love of my life. Thank you for letting me test my theories and hypotheses on you during all three of your pregnancies. You are the most beautiful pregnant woman in the world. In fact, from behind, you never looked pregnant.

I'd like to thank my daughter, Peace, and sons EJ and Uche. Thank you for being so well-behaved, warm-hearted, and kind in the womb (and outside). You are the greatest gift in the world and it's a privilege to be your daddy. Mommy and I love you so much. (P.S. If we mess up, let us know and we'll make things better or get you the very best therapy available.)

Thank you to my mom (Diane) and dad (Thomas) for creating me and to my mom for giving birth to me. I'd like to take this opportunity to formally apologize to you, Mom. Sorry I was two weeks overdue and that I had to be delivered via a surprise C-section. I don't know what I was thinking—if I could do it all over again, I'd have popped out at seven and a half pounds and saved you the scar. Who knows, I might even have a younger sibling had it been easier. Please accept my apology. I love you. And thank you, Dad, for being the best father in the world before you departed this world to make better plans for us in the next one. I love you and I miss you every day.

I'd like to thank my in-laws Tash and Bruce. I believe that if you could have given birth to me, you would have done it, but instead, you gave birth to my wife—and that's more than enough for me. Your constant love, support, and encouragement are a gift.

Thank you to my big brothers, Job, and Mike, and older sister-in-law Louisa—your wisdom, advice, guidance, help, love, and hand-me-downs. Thank you to my younger brother-in-law Aggrey and sister-in-law Ann. I hope, as your (BBIL) big brother-in-law, I can teach you the ways of the world. Thanks for all the love and always being there for us. Thank you to my nieces Thomas Jr., Rae, and Hannah and my nephews Dawson and Jeff. You have been the cutest and best practice babies for Mirabelle and me. I love being your uncle.

A heartfelt thank-you goes out to friends, family, and all the random contributors I accosted while researching this book. Thank you for opening up your lives and sharing your most personal, emotional, embarrassing, and deeply honest stories as part of this book. Your experiences are what make this project so compelling.

Thank you to all the doctors, nurses, and caregivers who helped us through pregnancy, labor, and delivery and the pregnancy, labor, and delivery of this book. My deepest gratitude goes out to my longtime editorial obstetrician, Kamal Ahmed, and my new editorial obstetrics team of Barwaqo Jelle and Prose Robert. You are all gifted handlers of thoughts, ideas, and words—thank you for helping me push and deliver this book from my womb (again, no editing). Thanks to Todd Strong (director of editorial obstetrics), and the editorial, sales, publicity, and support teams.

A heartfelt thank-you goes out to Rebecca Jones, the chief editorial obstetrician. Your passion, commitment, and encouragement are an inspiration. A thank you goes out to my agent/midwife, Lisa Green. You continue to be right there by my side throughout my personal and professional journey. Thank you to Glenn Mott and the entire team at King Features Syndicate, the newspaper editors who have supported my "Help Me, Alfie!" syndicated advice column over the years, the readers of "Help Me, Alfie!," the students and professionals who have invited me to share my passion on college campuses over the years, the Indiana University School of Journalism, the Indiana Daily Student, and the late Dr. Ishmael Sanda (still can't believe you're gone—I miss you).

Finally, thank you to the readers of this book. It's a privilege to have the opportunity to share this experience and time with you. I look forward to what I hope will be the beginning of a long relationship with you as you experience the most amazing, profound, surreal, and awesome adventure of your life.

Thank you!

Alfie Thomas.

FOREWORD

I have known Alfie Thomas for many years, and I am so excited to see his work finally published. His "expectant survival guide for first-time Dads through pregnancy journey" has been a long time coming, and it is something that the world needs now more than ever. In this foreword, I will briefly introduce him as an author and share some of my favorite thoughts of him as a friend. He is not only an amazing father but also one of the most inspiring people in my life.

Alfie Thomas was born in London England and moved to America when he was 16 years old to live with his mother's sister after being abandoned by his father at age 3. He went on to graduate from high school then served in the military before becoming a softtware engineer/writer/parenting coach/lecturer/Accountant.

As a father of three, he understands the challenges that come with parenting in today's world and has done his best to create an interactive guide for other parents trying their best to raise happy kids.

While at home I often find Alfie either playing hide-and-seek with his children or practicing magic tricks with them. He's an amazing father, and it is no wonder why his children love him so much.

NOTE ON TERMINOLOGY

"Wife, girlfriend, lover, he, she..." In an attempt to avoid offending anyone (an approach I've discovered usually ends up offending many people), throughout this book, the woman carrying your baby will be referred to as "your partner" Or "the mom-to-be". And because your partner is just as likely to be carrying a boy as a girl, we've alternated between "he" and "she" when referring to the baby (except where something applies specifically to boys or girls).

HOW THIS BOOK IS OUTLINED

To facilitate your understanding and guide you through each phase of your fatherhood journey, the book is divided into three parts.

The first part guides you on how to participate in ensuring both mom-to-be and your baby are safe during pregnancy and labor. The second part is about creating a strong bond between you and your child by caring for the baby at an early age (infantile age), and the third part is a comprehensive guide on techniques and practices to maintain your sanity, adopt proper financial discipline, grow a healthy father-child relationship, and raise a child that will stand out.

THE FIRST FATHER

THE EXPECTANT SURVIVAL GUIDE FOR FIRST-TIME DADS THROUGH PREGNANCY JOURNEY

INTRODUCTION

"Never is a man more of a man than when he is the father of a newborn."

— MATTHEW MCCONAUGHEY

"Wonderful!" was the only thing you said as you gently kiss her while looking deep into her eyes: careful not to reveal what is going on inside your head. "What do I do and how do I deal?"

Well, sit back and relax while I inform you of just what you got yourself into:

- Crying

- Sleepless nights
- Barely any free time
- Loads of money spent on something you will be constantly throwing away
- Confusion
- Concern

Am I being too honest for you? Well, if you are to survive what lies before you, you must be prepared with the tools and skills gleaned from the experiences of those who came before you (i.e. me and maybe a few others). Parenting is not easy. Especially if you're a first-timer.

Okay, this introduction was a bit 'tongue-in-cheek'. But most slapstick is based on reality, right? The truth is this: if you recognize the struggles that come with the territory and have the right perspective going into parenthood, the less surprised, better prepared, and more fulfilled you will be.

Some people say fatherhood is a natural instinct. Let's be honest, not all of us know how to be dads before we become one. I mean, be able to balance work, family, friends, hobbies...and everything else and raise an unstoppable child.

The first few years of fatherhood can be wonderfully soul-lifting and utterly awful. It is full of perfect moments, and terrifying ones. Being a first-time dad can be awe-inspiring and deeply frustrating - within the space of an hour.

Believe it or not, it takes effort and time to learn what it means to raise an outstanding child in today's day and age. I suppose that's why Jon Stewart said "Fatherhood is great because you can ruin someone from scratch". Because your baby is a part of you!

Fear not, as a father of one hot boy and two beautiful girls, I am here to tell you that every single struggle you go through is all worth it! If your first baby has not been born yet, then it may be difficult for you to comprehend the following sentence... Looking at your very own baby, touching your baby, holding your baby will open up feelings of love and compassion inside of you that you never knew existed!

It is this indescribable love that trumps all! All the sleepless nights, all the crying, all the banging-your-head-against-the-wall frustrations... they all mean nothing when you realize the precious miracle that is your very own baby!

However, pregnancy is a huge game changer for both moms and dads. It can be stressful, overwhelming, and full of worries about the unknown. Not only that, taking care of a baby and making sure they grow into a responsible human that adds great value to the world is a hefty task.

It is, therefore, important to know how to prepare yourself and your partner before the baby arrives so that you are ready for what life throws your way.

The good news is that there are many things you can do to make it easier for yourself and your partner-in-crime, and in the next several chapters, you will learn (step by step) guide on to survive your first-time fatherhood journey; from pregnancy to labor and early fatherhood, with as little stress as possible.

This is an easy read that walks you through the ins and outs of an expectant fathers as well as how to be a first-time dad. It will get you started on the right foot!

Let's dive right in...

BECOMING A FATHER - MY JOURNEY

I sat there as my thoughts kept racing up and down. I tried looking back at the last couple of years and what they had been like. We had been here a couple of times before since February of that year. But it had always been the usual visits. Nothing unusual. In fact, on a few occasions, I carried my laptop to continue working while we sat there waiting for our turn in the queue. Today, I could barely lower my head to read a Parents magazine that lay on the coffee table in front of me.

"Aaah...", she gasped in pain as she held onto her tummy. And before she could say what the problem was, I was on my feet looking for a nurse; to tell her I thought that this was now an emergency — officially. The time was 12.15 pm.

Earlier that day, we had woken up late and being a Saturday decided to continue watching an episode from the blockbuster, MoneyHeist, which is one of the very few series we've ever watched together.

My wife had graciously carried the pregnancy for the last nine months. And as is the norm, most days were tempered in nausea and exhaustion. Few of them, especially in the third trimester required a lot of walking, which she did graciously too. Sometimes we'd fight when I insisted that we do an extra 50 meters beyond the target. By and large, the pregnancy had been smooth, and I had the honor to experience the changes firsthand.

From the doctor visits to installing pregnancy app trackers that ensured I kept abreast with the ever-changing dynamics, to the ultrasound sessions where the sonographers kept telling us "See that — it's the stomach", they would say pointing on the screen at something we were sure wasn't a stomach. But what do we know? "Here is the skull, though it's not clear as the baby keeps moving a lot. Can you see it?" We would nod as if to confirm, in the same way, people nod to each other when they both don't understand the language involved.

At first, I tried following the transducer but never quite saw what the sonographer was touching. Then slowly I began to see the various parts. First, it was the legs, then the umbilical cord, another time I saw the eyes and the heart, then I saw the spine and other organs as the baby kept swimming around, seemingly oblivious of the perplexed onlookers.

So on this day, 3rd November 2014, as we sat there watching the series and having late breakfast, my wife suddenly announced that she had 'heard something dropping down there'. And from our voracious reading, it sounded like the mucous plug had come off. Meaning that we only had a few hours before the water broke. Otherwise, she would deliver in the house, with the only help being a software engineering graduate who hates the sight of blood.

In a span of 15 minutes, I had loaded the already packed maternity bag at the back seat of the car and we were off to Mater Hospital. We arrived there a few minutes after noon, and that's how we were both seated at the waiting bay, waiting to see a doctor.

We finally saw the gynecologist, who then proceeded to establish how far she had dilated. He looked back at our eager eyes before making the announcement — she was 2 centimeters!

Here we were, afraid that she had dilated to 9 cm, and would have actually delivered in the car while en-route to the hospital!

We were advised to proceed with admittance, after which we should start walking around the hospital as this helps in the dilation. Thereafter we spent the next 6 hours walking around the hospital, occasionally pausing to allow her to take in deep breaths as the pace of contractions rose. Often, I found myself walking a step behind her, in case she collapsed under her weight. I also had to deal with curious patients, doctors, and other onlookers, most of who cast mischievous gazes at us as if to say, "now you must lie on the bed you made alone".

At around 6.30 pm, we went back to the labor ward, as she needed rest. And there I found fellow men seated on the pews next to their wives' beds, in a remarkable show of solidarity. At this time, everything looked normal. No cries, apart from the occasional moans whenever the contractions would set in. For the first time, the process felt easier than I had expected.

Then we heard the first scream.

By 7.00 pm, the number of men in the labor room had considerably gone down. Only two of us now remained, and despite the curtains that shielded one from another, I could hear the other man next to us wishing his wife all the best, as he needed to go take care of their other children back at home. I almost drew the curtains and told him not to be a traitor. I was definitely terrified of being the only man sandwiched between the ladies and the furious contractions.

By 9.00 pm, anyone passing by our bed would have easily confused me for a professional masseur, as I neatly curved my hands around my wife's back massaging it to reduce the pains that accompanied the contractions, which by now were so frequent and predictable, she was literally waiting for them urging me to prepare whenever she felt them coming. "It's coming...! I can feel it...Rub my back harder... no, not there... Up here", she'd say, as I fumbled to follow her own hands, which now seemed to race all over. She had been in active labor from 7.30 pm until 9.15 pm when the doctors insisted that we help her limp into the delivery room. This was intended to help guide the baby into the pelvic opening which also encourages an optimal position for birth.

Inside the delivery room, I stared in utter disbelief as the doctors and nurses unleashed their arsenal as if preparing for the battle of the Titans. All this while, my wife maintained a brave face, which occasionally was interrupted rather painfully by the now consistent contractions that kept coming at her like a swarm of angry bees.

With the guidance of the nurses, I helped support her head, whenever she needed to push in the wake of a contraction, following the deep breaths. But just before

9.43 pm, I decided it was now time for me to also see where children come from, so I moved to the front where all the action was happening. And two minutes later, at exactly 9.45 pm, a small hairy purple handsome boy popped out!

He seemed deep in sleep, undeterred by the activities around him. But before the nurses could lift him up and slap his behind to usher in his first cry, he let out a loud scream, as they lifted him to cut off the umbilical cord. It was at this moment that I realized that I too, like my son, was crying uncontrollably. It was the first time I've cried so passionately in public without bothering to wipe off the endless rivers forming fast on my face.

After wiping and weighing him up, they moved him to a warmer at the corner of the room, where I also relocated, in readiness for our first ever conversation. "Welcome to earth, EJ", I said to him as I shook his miniature fingers. He had since stopped crying and was looked at me strangely as if to ask, "Are you sure you will be a good father to me?"

PART I

THE PREGNANCY SUPERSTAR

"More specifically being a dad is a diverse responsi-bilty, and it is also defined by providing support to your partner in the glorious journey of parenthood"

— NATALIE WEST

Quite often expectant fathers get bent out of shape over what they should be doing during the pregnancy. The pregnant woman is often the focus of all attention. She's the one carrying the baby. She's the one doctors examine. She's the one with oodles of books written especially for her. She's the one who has to push when the time comes and they put the baby on her belly when it is delivered.

So, the question is: Are you only along for the ride? Yes, you are only along for the ride. She's sailing the ship, but you are the entire crew. The research is resoundingly clear: A strong mate makes a difference. Having a supportive partner is good for everyone involved, including the baby.

All it takes is honing your powers of observation and intuition while capitalizing on the midas magic that you already have. My role is to guide you on how to unlock these powers and implement them.

Because Research shows that dads who are involved during pregnancy are more likely to remain involved once the baby is born—with great results. Kids with dads who are involved in their upbringing tend to do better socially, emotionally, and academically than kids with uninvolved fathers.

Moreover, from now until you snip the cord, a lot may happen that no one will have prepared you for ahead of time. There's no way to anticipate every possible scenario, but you need not be completely in the dark. It's also good to have an idea of ways you can be helpful to the mom-to-be.

In this part of the book, we'll focus on what you need to know about pregnancy, how you can prepare yourself for what is ahead, and the best possible ways to support your partner.

Your journey starts here. Let's call it "the journey to welcoming your little one"...

1

BASIC KNOWLEDGE OF PREGNANCY

"You can learn many things from having babies. How much patience you have, for instance."

— FRANKLIN P. JONES

The Stick Says "Pregnant". You know a major change is coming, but the only proof you have is a stick that says "Pregnant" or "+" or some arcane, ambiguous symbol that the instructions insist means she's pregnant. Just know that those sticks are almost never wrong, and your partner's gynecologist will do a blood test to confirm the pregnancy at her first appointment.

Hence, you must know a few basic things that accompany pregnancy. That way, it will be easier to differentiate between what's normal from what isn't. Also, your knowledge of pregnancy will guide you (greatly) on how to support your lady.

Enough of the noise... The first thing you should know is the pregnancy lingo, followed by how your baby develops and, lastly, the "Couvade Syndrome".

THE LINGO YOU NEED TO GASP

Birth positions

Imagine the Kama Sutra, but designed for arguably the least pleasurable experience possible – no jokes about sleeping with me, please. The traditional TV pose of 'lying on back' is considered less advantageous than squatting, or being on all fours, which can open the pelvis up to

30% more. This also helps restrict tearing. I lost you at "open the pelvis" didn't I?

Cervix

In the immortal words of our midwife, a cervix is a bit like the end of the balloon, which stops air from escaping – except it is holding a baby in the womb. Cue terrifying imagery of children fizzing across the room, or being turned into naff-looking inflatable dogs.

Colostrum

The early milk that arrives into your partner's boobs during pregnancy, ready for breastfeeding when the baby comes. This is a super-concentrated, super-thick serum-like fluid which provides your child's first meal, and is essential for their development. Let this be a warning to anyone who wants to be 'that guy' and try the milk before the baby arrives – the milk (proper) doesn't come into your partner's boobs until several days after birth.

Folic Acid

The vital vitamin you may never have heard of. It's recommended that your missus is popping these while you're preparing to get pregnant and through pregnancy – so a Viagra for you, a folic for her, maybe. Taking folic acid helps to protect against a whole host of issues. It's almost as important as spinach is to Popeye.

Isofix

Not a baby's savings account, but a baby-saving device which holds your car seat in place, locking into fittings in the back of most cars. Also known as LATCH in the US, and UAS in Canada, this savvy system was dreamed up as a quicker and easier alternative to securing car seats using a seatbelt.

Mamas & Papas

Your new favourite shop. You may as well set up a direct debit right now for 50% of your salary, and be done with it. Even the most hardened tightwad will struggle to take a trip to this store without absolutely spunking their load. Which is what got you into this predicament in the first place.

Meconium

Your baby's first poo. And, yes, it's supposed to be the appearance and texture of an oil spillage. Signs of this during labour can indicate that your baby's getting stressed, and will often encourage your midwife/doctor to hurry things along.

Paternity leave

Free holiday for dads! Well, kinda – if your holidays are spent working as a cooker-cleaner-shopper-insomniac. As standard, you will be entitled to one or two weeks leave on statutory pay of £140.98 or 90% of your average weekly income, whichever is lower. Your employer may have their own allowances, which can lessen the pay drop of the above. But not the lack of sleep.

Pitocin

Synthetic oxytocin used to induce labour by causing contractions, or after labour to slow bleeding. This injection is best known for induction and can fast-track stalling labours better than any curry, romp, or country walk.

Uterus

The pear-shaped bachelor pad that your baby will make their home during pregnancy. Which is kinda apt, given how pear-shaped your home life will go once they arrive. This organ pushes the baby out during labour, and expands from around 80g in non-pregnant women to almost a kilogramme at birth.

HOW YOUR BABY COMES ABOUT - MONTH-BY-MONTH

FIRST TRIMESTER

The first trimester will span from conception to 12 weeks. This is generally the first three months of pregnancy. During this trimester, your baby will change from a small grouping of cells to a fetus that is starting to have a baby's features.

Month 1 (weeks 1 through 4)

As the fertilized egg grows, a water-tight sac forms around it, gradually filling with fluid. This is called the amniotic sac, and it helps cushion the growing embryo.

During this time, the placenta also develops. The placenta is a round, flat organ that transfers nutrients from the mother to the baby, and transfers wastes from the baby. Think of the placenta as a food source for your baby throughout the pregnancy.

In these first few weeks, a primitive face will take form with large dark circles for the eyes. The mouth, lower jaw, and throat are developing. Blood cells are taking shape, and circulation will begin. The tiny "heart" tube will beat 65 times a minute by the end of the fourth week.

By the end of the first month, your baby is about 1/4 inch long – smaller than a grain of rice.

Month 2 (weeks 5 through 8)

Your baby's facial features continue to develop. Each ear begins as a little fold of skin at the side of the head. Tiny buds that eventually grow into arms and legs are forming. Fingers, toes, and eyes are also forming.

The neural tube (brain, spinal cord, and other neural tissue of the central nervous system) is well-formed now. The digestive tract and sensory organs begin to develop too. Bone starts to replace cartilage.

Your baby's head is large in proportion to the rest of its body at this point. At about 6 weeks, your baby's heartbeat can usually be detected.

After the 8th week, your baby is called a fetus instead of an embryo.

By the end of the second month, your baby is about 1 inch long and weighs about 1/30 of an ounce.

Month 3 (weeks 9 through 12)

Your baby's arms, hands, fingers, feet, and toes are fully formed. At this stage, your baby is starting to explore a bit by doing things like opening and closing its fists and mouth. Fingernails and toenails are beginning to develop and the external ears are formed. The beginnings of teeth are forming under the gums. Your baby's reproductive organs also develop, but the baby's gender is difficult to distinguish on ultrasound.

By the end of the third month, your baby is fully formed. All the organs and limbs (extremities) are present and will continue to develop to become functional. The baby's circulatory and urinary systems are also working and the liver produces bile.

At the end of the third month, your baby is about 4 inches long and weighs about 1 ounce.

Since your baby's most critical development has taken place, your partner's chance of miscarriage drops considerably after three months.

SECOND TRIMESTER

This middle section of pregnancy is often thought of as the best part of the experience. By this time, any morning sickness is probably gone and the discomfort of early pregnancy has faded. The baby will start to develop facial features during this month. Your partner may also start to feel movement as your baby flips and turns in the uterus. During this trimester, many people find out the sex (gender) of the baby. This is typically done during an anatomy scan (an ultrasound that checks your baby's physical development) around 20 weeks.

Month 4 (weeks 13 through 16)

Your baby's heartbeat may now be audible through an instrument called a doppler. The fingers and toes are well-defined. Eyelids, eyebrows, eyelashes, nails, and hair are formed. Teeth and bones become denser. Your baby can even suck his or her thumb, yawn, stretch and make faces.

The nervous system is starting to function. The reproductive organs and genitalia are now fully developed, and your partner's doctor can see on ultrasound if you guys are having a boy or a girl.

By the end of the fourth month, your baby is about 6 inches long and weighs about 4 ounces.

Month 5 (weeks 17 through 20)

Hair begins to grow on the baby's head. Your baby's shoulders, back, and temples are covered by a soft fine hair called lanugo. This hair protects your baby and is usually shed at the end of the baby's first week of life.

The baby's skin is covered with a whitish coating called vernix caseosa. This "cheesy" substance is thought to protect your baby's skin from long exposure to amniotic fluid. This coating is shed just before birth.

By the end of the fifth month, your baby is about 10 inches long and weighs from 1/2 to 1 pound.

Month 6 (weeks 21 through 24)

If you could look inside your partner's uterus right now, you would see that your baby's skin is reddish, wrinkled and veins are visible through the baby's translucent skin. The Baby's finger and toe prints are visible. In this stage, the eyelids begin to part and the eyes open.

The baby responds to sounds by moving or increasing the pulse. You may notice jerking motions if baby hiccups.

If born prematurely, your baby may survive after the 23rd week with intensive care.

By the end of the sixth month, your baby is about 12 inches long and weighs about 2 pounds.

Month 7 (weeks 25 through 28)

Your baby will continue to mature and develop reserves of body fat. At this point, the baby's hearing is fully developed. The baby changes position frequently and responds to stimuli, including sound, pain, and light. The amniotic fluid begins to diminish.

If born prematurely, your baby would be likely to survive after the seventh month.

At the end of the seventh month, your baby is about 14 inches long and weighs from 2 to 4 pounds.

THIRD TRIMESTER

This is the final part of your partner's pregnancy. You may be tempted to start the countdown till the due date and hope that it would come early, but each week of this final stage of development helps your baby prepare for childbirth. Throughout the third trimester, the baby will gain weight quickly, making your partner even more fat (which will help after birth).

NOTE:

Remember, even though popular culture only mentions nine months of pregnancy, your partner may actually be pregnant for 10 months. The typical, full-term pregnancy is 40 weeks, which can take into the tenth month. It's also possible that it goes past the due date by a week or two (41 or 42 weeks).

Your partner's healthcare provider will monitor her closely as she approaches her due date. If she exceeds the due date and doesn't go into spontaneous labor, the provider may induce labor using Pitocin.

THE COUVADE SYNDROME

It starts as a niggle in your tummy, maybe even a pain in your lower back, and you think, 'It's a tummy bug', 'Maybe I've just been overworking myself lately', 'It'll pass. But it never does. Weeks of throwing up become months, the awful smell of usually deliciously greasy foods becomes all the more unbearable and the back pain slowly but surely progresses to the rest of your body.

A question arises: "Am I also pregnant?" Yes, you're are... Oh sorry... Nope, you're not!. But chances are, you're not just sharing snacks — you're sharing symptoms too, along with at least half of all other dads-to-be.

Pregnancy symptom-sharing is so prevalent, researchers have dubbed it couvade syndrome, a French term that roughly translates to "we're pregnant." Read on to see how many of these sympathetic pregnancy symptoms resonate with you.

Anxiety

Even the most chill dudes can experience restless nights, heartburn, and bouts of fatigue while their partners are pregnant. Why? Turns out some men are much more likely to share pregnancy worries with their co-parent-to-be than others. Oddly enough, one study found that men who were either very distant from their own parents or who were very close were less likely to be stressed during their partner's pregnancy — but those who fell in between were more anxious.

How can you tame the tossing and turning? Reach out to other expectant dads, many of whom may be shaking in the same shoes as you. And don't think you can turn off the nerves by shutting out the pregnancy. Being more involved can make you feel better prepared and in control.

Nausea

Morning sickness isn't exclusive to mornings — or moms-to-be. While this infamous pregnancy woe is attributed to an uptick in a woman's hormones during pregnancy, men may also find themselves reaching for the saltines (or running for the toilet). But rather than estrogen being the culprit, male queasies are likely the result of the aforementioned anxiety as well as changes in diet, which are pretty common for men who eat to relieve stress. The cures: Get (or stay) physically active as a means to blow off steam, talk about what's worrying you with your partner or a friend, eat right, and watch your alcohol intake.

Mood swings

Don't be shocked if your partner goes through a Dr. Jekyll/Mr. Hyde routine a couple of times a day, especially between weeks six and ten, when hormones are surging through her body like a tidal wave. She may ping-pong between joy and sadness, tranquility and anxiety, and sweetness to (extreme) crankiness — and you may do the same. The fact is that while hormones intensify mood swings, the underlying cause is the same in both men and women: nerves.

As you've no doubt realized (likely in the middle of the night), having a baby is a big deal, and your life will never be the same. In many ways, it's changing already, which could lead to less sleep and even more mixed emotions. All this worrying is natural, and balancing out the highs and lows of becoming a new dad takes practice — so cut yourself some slack, Pop. There's no such thing as a perfect parent, and learning to accept that now is great practice for when the baby finally arrives.

Changes in Sexual Appetite

During pregnancy, a woman's sex drive can either rev up (lucky you) or shift into neutral — or do both within the same week. Some mamas-to-be experience a sexual surge (especially during the second trimester), while others are too tired, uncomfortable, or self-conscious about their bodies to be interested. But the male mojo is just as unpredictable right now: Some soon-to-be fathers are turned on by the changes in a pregnant partner's body, while others may find the transformation an overwhelming reminder of the responsibilities looming around the corner. Some men find themselves energized by the prospect of having a baby, while others are exhausted just thinking about it. And some expectant parents are too scared about hurting the baby to even think about having sex. (For most couples, there's no risk at all.)

If your sex life has stalled, try to remain intimate. Remember, sex is only one physical display of intimacy, and there are many other ways to be close without touching at all. A few tender tactics to try: Wake up a little earlier to have a morning cup of decaf together before work, take an evening walk (hand-holding encouraged), or snuggle on the couch with popcorn and a movie. The important thing is to find ways to communicate affection with your partner and share the new feelings you may both be experiencing...in and out of the bedroom.

Weight Gain

A bigger belly may be a given for a mommy-to-be, but why is it that a man gains an average of 14 pounds during his partner's pregnancy? Sympathetic snacking might be one factor, but that's not the whole story. A more likely culprit is cortisol, aptly dubbed the "stress hormone" because it's secreted at higher volumes during periods of anxiety. Cortisol regulates insulin and blood sugar levels, so your body may think it's hungry when it's not. Plus, cortisol directs where you pack on the pounds, which is — you guessed it — to the belly. Battle the bulge by stocking your kitchen with healthy snacks and watching your overall calorie intake. Also, consider amping up your exercise routine to reduce stress and your waistline.

Aches and Pains

Many symptoms of couvade syndrome seem to have clear causes, but others are more mysterious. Men consistently report toothaches, backaches, headaches, leg cramps, and other pains in various studies on sympathetic pregnancy. Some men even report experiencing pains in the same places at the same times as their partners. Researchers have yet to find any physical explanations for these simultaneous ouches, so the cause is likely psychological: Some daddies-to-be may be responding to subconscious feelings of competition (they might not be carrying a child, but they're becoming a parent, too). Whatever the case, treating what ails you with honest communication about the upcoming changes in your life is probably a lot more effective than popping a painkiller.

At least you know the Couvade syndrome... But hey, you're about to get even sicker. Below is what most men don't know about pregnancy:

2

PREPARE NOW OR PAY LATER

"PROPER PREPARATION PREVENTS POOR PERFORMANCE." STEPHEN KEAGUE.

In terms of preparing for fatherhood, most people think of tactical things. They think that new dad tips only involve changing diapers, holding the baby, or the best baby products to buy. While all these are great, you become experts on these things as time goes by. Preparing to be a dad more so involves mental preparation.

KNOW THESE & KNOW PEACE

I'd call these "The Unavoidable mental drainers" because I've heard people say "What you don't know can't hurt you". Well, this one might. If you don't know some of these basics and prepare yourself ahead, you'll likely learn the hard way later. Do yourself a favor and pay close attention while I tell you what no one else would.

It goes beyond preparing yourself for just a sick, tired, or moody partner. There are many things new dads must know about pregnancy that are not pointed out too often. This is the opportunity for you to learn more about pregnancy than you already know.

Luckily for you, I've made just about every single stupid mistake and placed my foot so far in my mouth during my wife's pregnancies that I'm overqualified to speak to you about things you need to know to avoid getting knocked out by the knocked up.

Here, we'll focus more on things that will leave you mentally drained. The aim is to prepare you mentally. Afterward, in the subsequent chapters, we'll dive deeper into ways you can prepare better and be a pillar for your partner (thank me later). The first thing I want you to know is that;

"Pregnancy Brain" is Very Real.

I know it sounds like some sort of cutesy, media-created term. But it's not. Pregnancy Brain is legit. It starts with everyday occurrences like looking for her glasses while they're on her head, which is kind of adorable. But it soon progresses to things like leaving the basement door open in 5-degree weather and freezing the entire bottom floor of the house while simultaneously leaving us susceptible to a home invasion. And in a fit of irony, I just asked my wife to give me more examples of Pregnancy Brain, but she couldn't -- because she can't remember.

Goodbye, sense of humor.

The good news is: she's gained a baby. The bad news? There wasn't enough room for the baby AND her sense of humor. If you're a smart-a** like I am, this is especially troubling, since I show affection by giving people good-natured sh*t. Unfortunately, my pregnant wife did not appreciate my unique brand of humor while carrying our little parasite around in her stomach. The results were often me firing off (what I considered to be) beautiful comedic quips and zingers, which didn't just fall on deaf ears -- they fell on potentially homicidal ears. You've been warned.

Say goodbye to sex, too.

Don't get it twisted. Sex is very safe during pregnancy (except where contraindicated by your doctor).

But listen to me carefully -- you're about to be sexually frustrated. The first trimester is by far the worst. It's when she'll be going through the most changes and feeling the sh*ttiest. It's everything she can do to avoid throwing up every morning (and sometimes at night), so your feeling unloved and "backed up" doesn't really register. The only silver lining is you'll have sex two times during the pregnancy. You have a one- to two-week window when her sex drive returns early in the second trimester. Enjoy that, because it's not happening again until very late in the pregnancy. Right at the end she'll be so desperate to get the baby out of her that she'll use you in the hopes that sex will send her into labor. It's slightly awkward, but after the drought it's a welcome relief -- as long as her water doesn't break right then and there.

Yes, her boobs are bigger; no, you can't touch them.

While we're on the topic of sex, let me tell you about one of nature's cruelest tricks. When a woman is carrying a child, it's a beautiful thing. That "pregnant glow" you always hear about is real, and it does wonders for her hair, her fingernails and -- her rack. A becomes C, B becomes D and C becomes Hallelujah Thank You God! They swell up to gargantuan sizes, literally breaking bras at the seams and popping off her chest in a fit of Playboy glory. The only problem is, you're not allowed to touch them. It's like going to the pet store and seeing the cute puppies behind the glass but not being able to pet them. They're adorable and you want to take them home and keep them forever, but if you try to motorboat her puppies she will slap the sh*t out of you. Trust me.

You will be replaced by pillows.

Did you spend a crap ton of money on a mattress? Some sort of memory foam or pillowtop deal that makes you feel like 1,000 little angels are massaging you as you fall asleep every night? Well, I hope you also spent money on a comfortable couch, because that's likely where you'll be sleeping for a decent part of the pregnancy. And it's not so much because of the increased space your pregnant wife takes up, either. It's the pillows. Yup, that's right. You become increasingly irrelevant as the pregnancy wears on, but the 37 pillows -- including that godforsaken full-body pillow -- become absolutely vital nighttime companions. And when push comes to shove, you're getting the shove to the sofa.

Don't treat her like glass.

Many men -- myself included -- feel very protective of their wives in general. But whenever our baby is growing inside of her, that protective instinct suddenly ratchets up several notches. I try not to let her open doors, carry groceries, pick up heavy objects, etc. And for whatever reason, that sticks in her craw something fierce. It's not that I don't think she can fend for herself; I just feel it's more important than ever to keep her safe, and to make sure the heavy lifting is kept to a minimum. And that's when I get the "I'M NOT MADE OF GLASS, STOP TREATING ME LIKE A PRINCESS!" retort. Oh well, husbands/boyfriends of pregnant women are damned if won't.

Pregnant women are lazy.

This one is VERY touchy and women love to deny it. They always say "We're not lazy, we're tired". After all, they're carrying new life around inside of them.

Their bodies are growing, stretching and changing to accommodate said life. But the fact remains, pregnant women are L-A-Z-Y. Case in point, a disturbing trend has emerged in the Daddy Files household during my wife's second pregnancy. My wife has not only stopped doing dishes, she's no longer even attempting to put the dirty dishes in the sink. Instead, she brings them into the kitchen and puts them a foot away from the sink. Moreover, all of the coffee cups are half-full and every bowl has a ton of soggy cereal remaining in it. I don't mind doing the dishes, but I do mind a counter full of crap. How hard is it to empty the dishes and move them ONE MORE FOOT into the sink?? But you can't gripe about this because...

Feed her constantly.

Everyone knows food is important to pregnant women. But what the uninitiated might not realize is that time is of the essence. The bottom line is, when she says she's hungry, she means it. Feed that woman immediately or she will eat your face. Know that "I'm hungry" doesn't mean she's looking forward to the dinner plans you have in an hour. It means give her a snack before you leave for the restaurant. And then again when you get in the car. Failure to promptly produce snacks will result in extreme b*tchiness at best, and bodily injury at worst. Just turn yourself into a walking, talking vending machine for nine months and you'll be fine.

What's yours is hers, what's hers is off-limits.

There's a good chance you've been married or together a few years now, so it's perfectly understandable that you bought into all that stuff about togetherness and sharing a life, etc. And while some of that still applies, all bets are off when it comes to food. If you eat food that's hers (or food you bought for yourself but she somehow claimed as hers), she will cut you. Not physically, perhaps, but by the time she's finished excoriating you you'll wish it was just a knife wound you suffered. I ate some of my wife's chocolate once, and when she went to find it during a craving and saw that it was gone, she flew into a rage that was one of the scariest things I've ever seen. Just don't do it.

You can't complain.

All these things I've listed? You can't mention any of them to your pregnant wife. Because even if she's lazy, not giving you any, won't let you touch her boobs, can't remember a thing, sleeping with the Pillow People, making you crash on the couch, putting on massive amounts of weight, and eating you out of house and home, it doesn't matter. She's pregnant. She's carrying your child. Which means she's got the trump card and all your complaints are hereby dismissed. Seriously, just think about you complaining and what her response will be. Something like "Dishes? You're complaining about dishes?? I'm growing a human being in my stomach the size of a watermelon that I'll eventually have to push out an opening the size of a lemon. NOW WHAT WERE YOU COMPLAINING ABOUT AGAIN?!?"

GET YOUR **S READY

I have a few simple ways you can prepare for fatherhood, but before I jump into my recommendations for how you should plan for fatherhood, I'll posit a famous yet brilliant African proverb, for it applies to parenthood every bit as well as it does to any winning strategy: "Tomorrow belongs to people who prepare for it today." Hence, I suggest that you ponder well and intentionally plan for what is ahead. Below, are some actionable steps to help you get started.

Practice with Real Babies!

Some guys are great with babies before they become fathers. Maybe they had plenty of baby-holding opportunities, maybe they were born with unwavering baby confidence, or maybe it's Maybelline. Who knows?

The majority of guys I know are scared straight when asked to hold a baby pre-fatherhood.

However, if you're preparing to be a dad, this is something I highly suggest you get comfortable with and lean in to. If you can get comfortable with someone else's baby, you're going to be sitting pretty once your little one comes along.

Take advantage of the opportunities that come your way. Don't shy away, maybe even ask to hold a friend's baby. Trust me, parents usually love when people are willing to hold their babies, even if it's just for a minute or two. (Just make sure you're not sick and have clean hands.)

Learn Your Calming Mechanisms

And no, I'm not referring to calming the baby. Unless your baby is the second coming of Christ, they will likely scream…a lot. Like, you can't even imagine how long and piercing this screaming will be. It was and still is one of the hardest things for me as a father to deal with.

When the crying becomes too much, my body goes into fight-or-flight mode and I instantly become a rage monster. Instead of what I would like to do (probably punch a wall), I resort to a personal calming technique I know will help.

Stepping outside for a moment and getting fresh air helps me immensely. Removing myself from the situation, breathing slowly, and processing my thoughts are helpful. I'm not normally the high-stressed type, but it's amazing what pterodactyl-like screams will do to a man's will.

Find your calming technique before the baby comes along so you know what to do when things become too much. Maybe it's working out or going for a drive (another of my favs). Maybe it's playing video games or watching a show you know will make you laugh. Whatever that thing is that will ease your mind and make things okay, do that thing.

Accept You Will Be Living With Less Sleep

I was so tired when we first brought home from the hospital that I tried to hand a phantom baby in the middle of the night to my wife, Mirabelle. I thought I was handing our daughter, Hanna, to Mirabelle and there was nothing in my hands. It was a hallucination. We laugh about it now, but it illustrates just how exhausted you become when you bring home a newborn.

There isn't a great way to prepare for less sleep. Everyone I asked before we had Hanna said I should just enjoy the sleep while I could. That was good advice. The best thing you can do is set the expectation low. Accept that you will be a walking zombie for a while and anything better than that is a win.

If you want a few practical tips, caffeine can be a lifesaver, and darkening your bedroom can increase the quality of your sleep (definite plus with limited sleep). I'm no specialist, but I think those two things are universal.

Talk With Other Fathers

Your feelings as a soon-to-be father or new dad are not new. It helps to speak with other dads who are going through the same thing as you or dads who have already gone through your new experiences. For one, you won't feel alone because you create a sense of community. Another benefit of talking with other fathers is the insights they can offer.

Having a community of people with shared experiences is valuable. With a support system ready to discuss the uncertainties of fatherhood, you can get through any difficulty because there are resolutions to the challenges you are facing.

You can rest assured that fathers will be enthusiastic about giving advice. Wanting to share knowledge and experiences is a human trait. For instance, if you find that your newborn sleeps better when you play some of your old records, you'd want to share that with a new father facing problems with putting their kid to sleep.

The Art of Misdirection

This is marvelous advice; don't take this for granted! Why a baby wants something is a mystery that will forever go unsolved. There are things your baby is going to want possibly just because you are holding it. If you want to keep said thing in your hand, you will need to distract your baby with another item. Normally, you will have your keys, cell phone, and wallet on hand. I have a saying, "Distractions are key, and keys make a great distraction."

One minute your baby will be throwing a tantrum and the next thing they know they are screaming for joy with shiny new keys in their hands. It sounds stupid, but clever misdirection is how magicians make their money from other adults. Entertainment is entertainment.

Increase Your Baby Knowledge

There are so many practical ways to prepare for fatherhood. Early on, your main job is responding to your baby's feelings and needs. If they are hungry, know what to feed them and how much. If they are bored, know what toys they like to play with or games they enjoy (e.g. peek-a-boo). And if they are upset, know what soothing techniques calm them down the best or what items will distract them from their frustration (e.g. car keys).

You won't be able to learn exactly how to calm your baby until they are born, but knowing multiple methods beforehand will save both you and your baby a lot of frustration in the beginning.

Beyond this book and any others you might've chosen, read everything from well-written blogs, to papers from the American Academy of Pediatrics, to fiction heavily focused on the father-child relationship. Go ahead and watch some family-centric shows and movies along with your reading. Also, joing facebook groups on fatherhood can help.

Prepare for Less Personal Time

Whether you recharge with time spent alone or you are a social butterfly who is revitalized by people, get ready for less personal time. As a very outgoing person that would spend every waking hour around friends or family if possible, I wanted to be the type of dad who wouldn't let having a child keep me from my social aspirations.

Unfortunately, I was very naïve. Children are a lot of work, and it's not a short process. Taking care of someone else makes it harder to fully take care of yourself. The time you would have spent reading that new book or going to the newest Marvel movie is now filled with diaper changes and your best rendition of Good Night Moon.

Take advantage of the sweet-sweet moments of personal time that come your way. I also highly recommend you communicate with your partner and schedule a personal time for both of you. This segues into my next tip...

Get Your Finances in Order

You might argue that finances are unrelated to mindsets or mental preparation for fatherhood. On the contrary, financial stress is a real problem that any new dads are worried about. Beyond saving money and not spending on useless things, you have to adjust your budget to accommodate a new life.

In the US, they say that it costs $240,000 to raise a child to age 17. Preparing for this challenge may require expert advice. Consult with a financial planner or advisor to help you plan for your new family's expenses.

Making smart financial decisions is not limited to working fathers. If you are younger and have limited resources, you still need a professional to help guide your decisions. Consider getting a better-paying job or finding a side hustle to earn extra income. The early stages of fatherhood can be stressful, so you want to reduce as many potential issues as you can before the child arrives.

Turn "I Have To" Into "I Get To".

Instead of having an "I have to" mindset, shift into an "I get to" mindset. For instance, if you find yourself saying "I have to feed the baby," you can say "I get to feed the baby." Or turn "I have to go to the appointments with my wife" into "I get to learn more about my future child." Change your mindset to create opportunities out of your newfound fatherhood.

Think of fatherhood as a blessing that you are grateful for. "Thank goodness I get to be a dad!" When you express your gratitude, you are creating a positive impact on your life. We believe that you cannot be depressed if you are grateful. In that sense, gratitude is the antidote to depression.

Check the Influence Around You

Motivational speaker Jim Rohn used to say that you are the sum of your five closest friends. So, reassess the company you keep. Do you surround yourself with people who make good decisions? Do they take good care of themselves? Do they treat other people well? You may need new friends if you answered no to any of these questions.

As a new father, your environment will change. Some aspects of your life that made sense up to one point may no longer serve you the way they used to. Take partying for example. Before fatherhood, you loved to party with your friends. As a new father, partying may not be as interesting anymore. You'll have to make the choice to adapt to that change.

Think of these adjustments to your environment as necessary steps for your child's future environment. You are essentially building your child's immediate world with the company you keep. Your environment will dictate who and what your child interacts with, so you must be mindful of external influences.

Be Okay With Mistakes

You must understand that mistakes are inevitable and normal. As a new father, you have to learn to be okay with your mistakes. Forget about lacking self-confidence and being hard on yourself when you make a wrong step. All the mistakes you've made prior to having your child will seem irrelevant compared to the mistakes you will face as a new father.

Successful fatherhood has no room for ego. We are meant to make mistakes, accept them, learn from them, and then move on from them. It's a constant cycle. We've all held the baby wrong, changed their diaper wrong, or dressed them backward. Mistakes to the tactical things are fixable. We must focus on minimizing the mistakes related to our mindset and how we raise our children.

3

PITCH IN - HELP MOMMY TO SAVE THE BABY!

Remember, we all stumble, every one of us. That's why it's a comfort to go hand in hand.

— EMILY KIMBROUGH

My father explained to me when I found out my wife was pregnant, that I was going to have to be mentally strong for her as well, and allow her to lean on me in the tough times. I told him I understood, but I truly didn't understand until the day we left the midwife's place and had the biggest scare of our pregnancy.

Our midwife told us that if there's any problem with the ultrasound, that she would give us a call, but if there was not, that we wouldn't hear from her. While I was ironically cleaning the house, she called and left a message before I could get to the phone. My heart was racing, because I remember the words she had said to us before we left the office.

I went to get my wife, and we nervously waited for her to call back. My wife had a number of fears going through her head, and I had to do everything I could to try and remain strong and assure her that things were going to be okay. Her face was turning ashen, she was so stressed out. It only took about 15 minutes for the midwife to callback, but it seemed like forever. Apparently, my wife had a low-lying cervix, and we just had to wait for it to move, which thankfully it did as the pregnancy went along.

This is just a an example of instances that happened during the pregnancy that gave us a scare. As an expectant new dad, you will have to learn how to be the rock that your partner can lean on in these times.

By now, you should've realized that pregnancy is an intense experience. A woman's body undergoes a lot of changes, some physical but many emotional. It can also be a time where couples feel disconnected or less close than before they were expecting.

When you are an involved father from day one, your relationship with your partner tends to be better. She feels like she has a solid ally and is not going into this venture alone. Just as the Turkish people say;

"No road is too long with good company".

Besides, do you think what affects Mom will affect your child? Think about it. That baby is insider her. To some extent, on some level, your positive relationship with your partner will get into that womb.

As you are about to see, mom-to-be will truly appreciate your support and the two of you can develop a teamwork approach to parenting from these early stages.

In this chapter, you will learn how to support your partner throughout pregnancy so that you can have an enjoyable journey together. You will be there for her every step of the way, from morning sickness to mood swings.

Meanwhile, let's first run through her mind and hear what she has:

YOUR PARTNER'S MIND IS EXPOSED!

"I'm going, to be honest with you, so don't judge me and hate me. I would really still like you to buy me those donuts you promised this morning... even after you read this.

Pregnancy is such a beautiful journey that two people go on together. Yes, it includes you, my dear expectant daddy. But it's also a very stressful, crazy, whirlwind, and sometimes rough time in our lives.

I've experienced feelings and symptoms that I've never felt before.

Not everything is about me and what I want or need during this time. It's also about us, our bond, our love, and the little miracle growing inside me that we created together!

I need your support, your affection, and for you to communicate with me every step of the way. WE are a team and WE are in this together.

I know it may be hard for you right now because I push you away at times and it honestly feels like I'm not the woman of your dreams, but the truth is... my hormones are raging!

I feel like I have an alternate personality at the

moment and I really can't control it. I promise you, I feel like crying (for you) as I speak. It's a challenging time for you, I know.

But hey, some days I feel like I want to punch you in the face while other days I wish you grabbed my hand and kissed me when I least expected it.

Some days I think about having sex in odd places while other days I wish your penis never existed.

Stop asking me if the baby is hurting while we having sex... trust me, the baby can't feel your penis.

My boobs may have gotten bigger but that doesn't mean you can touch them whenever you want. You might end up getting replaced with a pregnancy pillow at night.

I know that you think that I am a difficult person to deal with right now but please understand – I am swollen, hungry, gassy, and tired. The last thing on my mind is having a quickie when I can't even see how my vagina looks like right now.

Most days, I don't feel pretty.

Sometimes even I can't explain how I am feeling but all I know is that I need you to keep telling me that I am beautiful even when I'm lying on the hospital bed in tears and pain about to birth our child.

I need you to surprise me when you can – spoil me with a foot massage or cook dinner for us.

There is a little human growing inside me – a little

person who takes a lot of my energy – physically and emotionally.

I need food, feed me constantly. And no, I cannot share it with you.

Being a mom is exhausting. Some days I just wait for you to ask me: "What can I help you with right now my darling?"

Is this too much to ask for?

I'm getting fat and lethargic. I am not being lazy so don't rub it in.

Help me with the daily chores and come with me to doctor's appointments.

Take me to a movie or let's go for a weekend away and indulge in delicious food that I've been dreaming about.

I want to spend as much time as I can with you before everything changes all over again.

Talk to my belly and sing to your baby (don't worry; your melodious voice doesn't suck).

I know you will enjoy feeling those tiny kicks too.

Share my excitement and help me prepare.

I know I've been going overboard with storage containers.

But Nesting is serious business.

Sometimes I feel like I'm losing my mind because I'm not sure if I bought what I went to the store to buy.

I know this is scary for you but it's also scary for me. I didn't realize how much gas I had until now.

My sense of humor doesn't exist anymore.

I didn't imagine crying in a store over washing powder that was out of stock would be a reality. But it's happening.

I'm starting to waddle when I walk.

I cry when things don't happen the way I want them to.

I cry when things happen the way they are supposed to.

And,

I scream at you for absolutely nothing.

But I still love you.

Remember there will be good and bad days... but I need you to get through them all.

Just be there – Have lots of tissues, love, and patience... and if you want to know a little secret – along with the tissues always have my favorite snack. Even if it may change, I will know that you are always thinking of me.

Let's enjoy this rollercoaster ride .... TOGETHER. Good luck my darling... Muah!"

FIRST TRIMESTER: WEEK 1 -13

The first trimester of pregnancy can be a tough time for both you and your partner. She is expending a lot of energy building a baby's body during this time and it's common for her to want nothing more than sleep all day long. Her senses are heightened so certain smells and taste might make her nauseous while hormones rage through her system making mood swings happen with ease - take comfort knowing that morning sickness usually subsides by week 14 which also coincides when most women will have their energy levels completely return back to normal too! Below are some ideas on what you can do during this period:

Antenatal care visits

The care you give your partner during this time will have impacts for years to come. With tight work schedules, I understand that this may be difficullt. But when possible, accompany your partner for her antenatal appointments. Keep close tabs on her progress. Watching your little baby during a scan, kicking away on the screen as you hear the rhythm of his little heartbeat with your the mom can be a wonderful bonding exercise.

Sometimes they seem like unimportant appointments, but there can be moments when she receives unexpected news. You don't want her to be alone during such times.

If you can only attend a few, go for the ultrasounds and be sure to call her after all the others to show her you care.

Reading and discussing

It's always a nice way to spend some time together, and you'll both learn more about the process along the way! Keep track of the pregnancy, including creating a scrapbook of different milestones and the feelings felt during pregnancy. Use a journal as a fun way to share special moments. There are also plenty of video resources out there too if reading isn't your thing or it just doesn't fit into your schedule.

Listen and observe.

It is one thing to hear your partner...it is another to listen. Simply listening to how she feels, her fears, her worries, and any of her anxieties about pregnancy is helpful in itself. She knows you don't have all the answers, but she may still need to vent to someone about what she is dealing with.

On a deeper level, do you feel you came away from the conversation with a better understanding of their positioning? Do you feel they came away from it with a better understanding of yours? Do you feel concerns were addressed and a mutual conclusion determined? Did a positive shift occur in you and/or your partner's body language to indicate that the discussion was resolved satisfactorily?

Before moving on another topic of discussion, verify that all parties feel heard. Listen to the words and language used, reflect on the body language exhibited, and welcome any follow-up discussion as needed.

Feeding Her.

Before you go your separate ways for the day, indulge in a nice breakfast together. You can choose to make something at home or go check out a new breakfast eatery in your neighborhood.

Otherwise, you should know that an empty stomach can up the nausea, so make sure she has a healthy snack (trail mix, a granola bar) stashed on the nightstand to nibble on when she wakes up. Everything she's eating, make sure it is healthy, nutritious food that's easy to digest so she can feel her best each day.

If nausea becomes a problem, try making recipes without strong smells or tasting salty and spicy foods.

Lighten Up And Clear The Way.

One way to make the bathroom an easier place for Mom is by installing nightlights. This will help her see better and avoid any accidents on dark pathways at nighttime or in dimly lit hallways. To prevent confusion, it's also important to clear a path from her bedroom door all the way into the main lavatory area so she can easily find it without error when she needs relief during inconvenient hours of day time or night-time.

THE SECOND TRIMESTER: WEEK 14 -27

You know what they say: when it rains, it pours. Your wife's pregnancy has been difficult enough with morning sickness and fatigue. During this time, the morning sickness should be gone, she will have a little more energy and her mood swings are less intense, but now that the second trimester is underway she's experiencing a whole new set of challenges. She'll have trouble sleeping at night because your unborn baby is demanding more space in there, and she may experience heartburn or leg cramps as well! The good news is that you can still do a lot to help your pregnant partner during this time.

Feel Your Baby (On Consent).

Something as subtle and beautiful as a baby's first movements can only be felt by the mother. What does it feel like when you know your unborn child is moving? Incredible!

I remember my own mom telling me about her experience cradling us in utero while she slept on the couch or walked around town shopping for clothes to prepare our arrival into this world. I was very young at the time but still have vivid memories now - how we kicked less often during certain times of day, what positions were best for restful sleep (she always said not too much lying down), which foods helped settle tummy aches after eating.

If you don't want to be left out, then get a front row seat to your baby's performance by placing your hand on her belly. You will be able to tell if the kicks are strong or gentle, and you can also count them! Also, talk/sing to your baby. Hearing your voice helps your baby feel attached to you quickly once he/she is born.

Make Her Sleep Better

Raising your pregnant partner's head and shoulders on a pillow while she sleeps can help alleviate pain in her back or hips.

The benefits of sleeping with the right support include better breathing, which may lessen snoring; relief from acid reflux symptoms like heartburn and nausea that might otherwise keep you up at night; less pressure on joints such as knees and wrists - all thanks to an extra set of hands so one person doesn't have to do it alone!

Give Her a Belly Rub.

Your partner's bump is growing bigger, and so the skin stretches. It can be dryer or itchy as a result of this change in size! Rub shea butter or any other moisturizing creams on her belly to alleviate these issues for your partner. This would also make an excellent way to pamper them if they are feeling uncomfortable with their changing figure while pregnant!

THE THIRD TRIMESTER: WEEK 28 -40

The third trimester is an intense time for pregnant partners. It can be a struggle to help your partner through her discomforts, and she may need more support than ever before! For example, the baby's weight becomes really heavy towards the end of pregnancy; tiredness and irritability often return as well- you might even notice that peeing will become frequent (it won't stop!). Pregnancy brain also occurs during this phase of the pregnancy.

Washroom watchout.

You can prevent a lot of falls and mishaps by installing handrails in the shower. They're inexpensive, easy to install, and will provide your loved one with much more independence when it comes time for them to get out of the bath or adjust their position while bathing. You may also want to roll up area rugs or tape down carpets so that slipping is less likely if they do happen to fall over on these surfaces.

Pack your hospital bag.

Your bag is just as important as hers. You should have your bag packed by week 36 because babies don't always come on schedule. Bring a change of clothes, toothbrush and toothpaste, snacks and drinks, something to keep you occupied, digital camera and most importantly your mobile phone and all other dad's survival kit.

Disconnect to connect.

Schedule some time together during the week and turn off your phone, tablet, and other devices. When you do so, you are making a conscious decision to connect with your partner. You are prioritizing time with your partner over checking out the newest posts on social media, giving your relationship a much-needed boost. Want to make it extra special? Talk about why you love your partner and what you are looking forward to as you welcome your new baby.

Sieze the baby-less moments

Let's face it - errand runs are monotonous and we often dread carving out time to get them done during the week. Why not ask for a little company to make the experience more enjoyable? Have a grocery list that must be tackled? Do it together. Need to pick up her prescription? Turn it into an outing. Got a gift that you need to mail for your best friend's birthday? Grab your partner's hand and head to the post office. Going on errand runs together gives you an opportunity to steal moments throughout the week. It's a chance to catch up on what you both have done during the week and what you are looking forward to next week.

Write love notes.

We are taking this old-school! Plan an activity where you exchange love notes every day during a designated time. Maybe you want to do it in your third trimester as you prepare for two to become one. Grab a post-it note and a pen and write a sweet message to your partner. Your partner should do the same. At the beginning of every day during this designated time, exchange your written love notes but do not open them right then and there. Open them later in the day when you are apart. You and your partner can talk about what the notes meant to you after you have finally opened them. Save them to a scrapbook if you wish to preserve them.

Install your baby's car seat.

you can't drive home from the hospital without a car seat and they can be complicated to install, so don't wait till the very last minute. If you're having trouble, get help from an authorised restraint fitting station.

Fill up the freezer.

Save your future self some serious kitchen time by stocking up the freezer with healthy meals before the arrival of your baby. It's a major stress reliever not having to prepare meals in the first 2 weeks if you do not have family around to cook for you.

OTHER WAYS YOU CAN SUPPORT YOUR PARTNER

Compliment her.

Your partner's body is going to change during pregnancy and there is no way to avoid that. She may struggle with this and she may be fine and embrace it. Regardless, compliment your bunny often. Tell her how pretty she looks, how she is glowing, or how happy she has seemed lately in her element of baby planning. Whatever it may be, do not underestimate how important it is to compliment your partner.

Don't comment on the nesting.

You may wonder who came in and replaced your once normal partner with this woman whose idea of fun is cleaning baseboards and the inside of the dishwasher on a Friday night but just go with it. supporting mom-to-be during pregnancy sometimes just means you let her nest. Nesting, aka cleaning and preparing for the baby, is a normal part of pregnancy. Just roll with it because you'll have a cleaner house because of it! If you're feeling like you can keep up with her cleaning frenzy, offer to pitch in!

Be enthusiastic about the birthing classes.

Birthing classes don't exactly sound like something you'd want to sign up for or get excited about but don't make too many complaints about this. Childbirth is already something she has to undergo herself and she may be very nervous about it. Do your best to be supportive and enthusiastic about any class that is going to help put your partner's mind at ease–you may even learn something yourself!

Allow her some "me time".

Arrange for a night where you leave the (already clean!) house for her so she can simply relax with some peace. Encourage her to go to a spa or get her nails done. As much as she loves you, sometimes the hormones she's dealing with leave her feeling too tired to even interact. So watch out for these moments and let her know your planning to get out of her hair for just a few hours so she can do whatever she wants!

Do the dishes.

Or the laundry...or the vacuuming...you get the idea. Anything you think you can do to help out around the house will be much appreciated by your tired consort who is working harder than she even realizes to grow a new baby. After a long day dealing with a changing body and hormones, even the smallest household chores can feel like a mountain to a pregnant woman. So keep an eye out for those little things!

Indulge on occasion.

Your partner may be trying her best to stay active and healthy during her pregnancy, but there are always those few occasions where a craving just needs to be satisfied. Humor her and enjoy running out for milkshakes together. It will make her feel better and at least you can share these moments. You probably don't want to fully gain sympathy weight, but if you do, at least you are in it together!

Bond over hobbies and interests.

If you have an interest in a particular topic or activity, share with your partner. For example, if you love history documentaries and notice an interesting one that is premiering next week, turn it to a movie night. It's okay if she doesn't like it. Understand that she can be moody or have preference. If possible, opt for her choices. Be open to your partner if they make the same request. When couples connect through a passion, it can lead to a deeper intimacy. For example, if your partner enjoys completing puzzles, ask if you can join them. Working together towards a common goal can lead to feelings of fondness and mutual respect.

Have in-depth conversations about parenting.

Now is a great time to talk about your excitement and concerns about the future. Consider talking about how you might want to parent - maybe you are considering an authoritarian parenting style while your partner is leaning more towards an authoritative parenting style. Or maybe you find attachment parenting concepts interesting, like co-sleeping, while your partner is envisioning that your child will sleep in their own room after birth. Either way, you can intimately connect with your partner by talking about how you hope to parent collaboratively and effectively. You do not have to have it all figured out today, tomorrow, or next month, but this conversation can provide good food for thought as you walk into this next stage.

Talk baby.

It can feel like your to-do list is never-ending when you are supporting your partner during pregnancy. From baby names to nursery themes to finding the right pediatrician, you may find yourself overwhelmed by the sheer number of things that must be done before your little one comes home. Sit down and write out what you hope to accomplish before that point. Talk about things that you are both excited and concerned about as you tackle this list. During these conversations, you may talk about who the baby might look like or whose personality they will have. She may discover that you are nervous about diapering the baby properly while you may confide that you worry about how to get the baby settled into a routine. Once you have these excitements and concerns out in the open, this is a chance to really bond.

Be honest.

During this time, you may feel a lot of emotions, some positive and some negative. Discuss them as they come up so you and your partner are on the same page. If you have a concern about something your partner has or has not done, talk about it up in a way that you are focused on finding a solution to the problem. By focusing on a solution to the problem, why the solution is necessary, and not your partner specifically, you can acknowledge what is upsetting you while also making steps to move forward in a constructive way.

4

THE P'S AND Q'S OF PREGNANCY

.

"It is better to be safe than sorry"

— SAMUEL LOVER

You already know that before your little bundle of joy arrives, you and mama are responsible for helping them grow in a nurturing, healthy environment.

This probably leaves you with a lot of questions and worries about possibilities; from what your woman can eat, to the foods she should avoid, whether she can keep on with her exercise, and how to have sex again.

While you can't prevent every possible complication, I will share with you a list of what to do and what to avoid during pregnancy to help reduce pregnancy complications and keep your baby healthy.

HAVE SEX IF SHE'S UP FOR IT

Sex is an essential part of a healthy relationship, and pregnancy does not have to put a damper on your sex life. You may be wondering if it is safe to have sex during pregnancy or if you will hurt the baby by having inter-course. The answer is no! Unless your partner's health care provider has told her otherwise, you can have sex throughout the entire 9 months. Sex is not harmful because the baby is protected within the uterus and cushioned by fluid.

Besides your doctor's warnings, there are also other situations when you could not have sex with your pregnant partner. While these are basically commonsensical considerations, it remains practical to still point the obvious, such as:

- Having a history of miscarriage or premature birth
- The placenta is covering the cervix (this is Placenta previa in medical terms)
- Her water has broken
- She is having bleeding problems
- Your (or your partner's) religious belief or cultural upbringing about pregnancy sex (if ever there is such a thing)
- Either you, or your partner, has sexually-transmitted disease (told you, these are obvious considerations).

SOME SEX POSITIONS YOU COULD TRY:

Wife on top

While some men may complain that they feel helpless when the woman is on top and is the one in control, this position works best during pregnancy as your wife can control how deep you penetrate inside her. She is also in control of how fast or slow the session will be.

On all-fours

This is sometimes referred to as "doggy-style." At the early stages of pregnancy, this could actually be one of the most preferred positions. The wife does not have to exert much effort and there is no direct pressure on the tummy. However, when the belly becomes bigger, it would be heavier and it might get pressed against the bed or pressed between her legs and upper torso. As long as she could keep her belly raised, this would work as just one of those position for a shorter time before switching to another position.

Spooning

This could be one of the most erotic and sensual positions lovers could have. The woman sits in front of the man who is also in a seated position. There is no pressure on the stomach, and the man could reach in front for added stimulation to his partner's erogenous zones.

Lying on one side

This position frees the woman's back from pressure, and the tummy is safely supported by its side. With one leg raise, the man could enter from either behind or he can be position perpendicularly (like a letter "T" position) and penetrate while facing her. This could be a tricky position at first but once you get the hang of it, you'd find that this is less strenuous for both of you.

If, for some reasons, you can't do any of the above, the simple but very intimate mutual stimulation of the partner's sex organ would do the trick.

IF SHE'S NOT UP FOR SEX:

Talk.

Maybe your partner wants other intimate gestures, like kissing and cuddling, more than sex. That's okay! Like I said, your partner's desire for intimacy and sex in general can shift during pregnancy. With all of the changes that are happening to her, she may not be as interested in the sex life as she used to be in the past.

Sit down and talk about it to get ahead of any incompatibility issues that may arise going forward. If you are unsure how to communicate what you are feeling and need insight into how to communicate, consult with a therapist who specializes in families and relationships for help finding the right words.

Hug it out.

Embrace your partner when you can and enjoy the feeling. You don't have to talk or escalate to anything more if your partner does not want to do so. Hugs, and other intimate acts like kissing and sex, cause our body to release oxytocin. Oxytocin is also known as the "cuddle" or "love hormone". Not only is a nice, cozy, and long hug a great way to get closer to your partner, it is also reduces your anxiety levels. So reach for your partner and encourage them to do the same!

Indulge in a DIY couples' massage.

Grab a luxurious bottle of massage oil, dim the lights, lay down, and take turns massaging each other. This intimate act is a wonderful way to connect physically without having sex. If you want to emulate a spa setting, you and your partner can turn on some soft jazz, put a few drops of lavender oil in an oil diffuser, and set up nice, soft sheets on your bed. Focus on keeping the massage loving and slow for the ultimate evening. Want to make the DIY massage extra special? Light candles, or better yet, use battery-operated tea lights. If you want to use candles, just remember to keep an eye on them and blow out when you are done.

INDULGE IN EXERCISE

Staying active during pregnancy is important for expecting moms. The various benefits of simple exercises during pregnancy include pain management, mood regulation, better sleep, and preventing excessive weight gain. In addition, a small new study showed that prenatal aerobic exercises could lead to healthier weight in babies.

Of course, it goes without saying that doctors should be consulted before undertaking any workout routine to prevent untoward incidents.

They have to be careful not to do anything that's too strenuous, gets their heart rate up too high or increases their body temperature too much. Below are a number of workouts you and your partner can do that won't overstress the already-sore joints.

Yoga

Prenatal yoga can help a mom-to-be deal with the changes her body endures during pregnancy notes the American Pregnancy Association (APA). The poses are designed to increase flexibility and strengthen muscles while helping to develop breathing and relaxation techniques that could help a woman get through labor.

It can also include improved sleep along with decreased lower back pain, nausea and headaches while also reducing the chance of preterm labor.

Hot or Bikram yoga are not recommended for pregnant women due to the hot environment class is conducted in.

Stationary Bikes

Like swimming, bicycling is one exercise that doesn't cause unnecessary body stress, since the bike supports the woman's weight according to the APA. The risk of falling is also reduced when biking. And, it's a year-round exercise since, most gyms have stationary bikes.

Intense spin classes, however, are not recommended for pregnant women, since they can get pretty hot and raise your heart rate.

Walking

Don't underestimate how beneficial walking can be. It's easy to work into your schedule and doesn't take a toll on your knees like running can. Be sure to wear comfortable shoes, notes the APA, while setting realistic distance goals.

Swimming

Hop in the pool with your partner and give swimming a shot. Swimming provides an overall body workout without putting stress on joints. It also helps raise the heart rate without the risk of overheating.

A swim is also a good way to cool down if her third trimester happens to be during the hot summer months.

HELP MAMA GRAB SOME SLEEP

According to "science," if you live for 75 years, you will spend 25 of those years asleep. Unless you have a pregnant partner at any time during those 75 years, in which case you will actually sleep for 24 years and 3 months. But, wait, that actually probably doesn't account for after the baby is born, so subtract at least another 3 years. Oh, and then they'll be reckless teenagers, so maybe shave off another 4 years. You know what? Forget it. Who needs sleep anyway?

Well, actually, your pregnant partner needs sleep. But it turns out that growing a human is pretty restless work. Luckily, there are some things you can do to help her get some shut eye, none of which include telling her your boring theories about the MLB post-season. Though that might work too.

Help Her Keep A Schedule

After having the baby, you'll learn quickly that sticking to a strict schedule is crucial for getting your kid to sleep. So you might as well start practicing with your partner now, because it turns out a regular sleep schedule will help her too.

So when bedtime rolls around, maybe try not to pressure her into just one more episode of Narcos. But feel free to skip the lullabye and the reading of Goodnight Moon.

Help Her Reduce Anxiety

She might already be into yoga and mindfulness meditations, which'll help her de-stress. But you have something that she hasn't got: some strong magic fingers (and they're 'uge so guaranteed no problem there). What are they good for? Some good old-fashioned prenatal-massage.

Beyond that? Try not to talk about nervous-making baby issues before bed. Topics like what to expect from prenatal testing a best left for the morning, much like high fiber cereals.

Help Her With The Meals

Cooking can be a hassle. If you're tired from a whole day of gestating, it can be tough thinking about digestion. Which can lead to processed meals and indigestion. That's no good for sleepy times.

So go ahead and man the stove, man. Try some non-spicy recipes that avoid anything that requires being submerged in hot fat — bonus points for some added folic acid. You can sneak in some wings when you're out with your bros, but making some good meals for her now will help her heart burn only for you.

Deal With Your Snoring

Your nighttime breathing exploits sound like a dog fight. That's not only disturbing, it's downright unethical. If there was ever a time to fix your ridiculous schnoz-racket, it's before sleep gets really dicey in the third trimester.

Try elevating the head of the bed (which might help her too) or using those nasal strips. If things are truly jacked, get your doc to hook you up with a self-administered at-home sleep study and go from there.

THINGS TO AVOID (THE DON'TS OF PREGNANCY)

Undercooked, Raw, And Processed Meats

You might have heard that pregnant women should avoid deli meats, and that's true! That's because deli meat (and lunch meat, hotdogs, and other processed meats) can become contaminated with bacteria during processing, packaging, or storage. These bacteria can threaten her health.

In addition, bacteria can lead to serious health problems for your baby, including severe neurological illnesses (like blindness, epilepsy, or intellectual disability). In extreme cases, these bacteria can even cause stillbirth.

To ensure both mom and baby are safe from these dangerous bacteria – such as E. coli, Salmonella, Listeria, and Toxoplasma, you should encourage mama to stop eating undercooked or raw meat during pregnancy. It's best to make sure the meat is completely cooked through.

Alcohol

Pregnant women are strongly urged not to drink alcohol during pregnancy. This substance can cause many complications during pregnancy, have damaging effects on developing fetus, and may contribute to other medical problems as your child grows.

When a pregnant woman drinks alcohol, it travels through her bloodstream and into the fetus. That means that when mom has a glass of wine, your baby has a glass of wine, too. In addition, drinking alcohol can lead to eating less, thus losing sources of nutrients.

Furthermore, alcohol consumption during pregnancy can cause what is known as fetal alcohol syndrome (FAS). FAS includes mental and physical birth defects and growth problems associated with the mother's high levels of alcohol use during pregnancy.

Smoking

The same rule applies to smoking. Smoking is dangerous to your baby during and after pregnancy, and makes it harder for mom to recover from delivery. Smoking deprives the fetus of oxygen, which can also lead to accelerated ovarian aging; a higher risk of miscarriage, and low birth weight babies.

What's more? Once your baby is born, there is a higher likelihood of the child having developmental issues like mental and behavioral problems.

Fresh-squeezed Juice

Pregnant women should opt for juice that is pasteurized. Fresh-squeezed juice in restaurants, juice bars, or farm stands may not be pasteurized to protect against harmful bacteria, including salmonella and E. coli. Some markets also sell raw, unpasteurized juice in the refrigerated case — look for the required warning label, and steer clear. Juice in boxes and bottles on your supermarket shelf is also safe.

Raw Eggs

Raw eggs or any foods that contain raw eggs should be avoided because of the potential exposure to salmonella. Some homemade Caesar dressings, mayonnaise, homemade ice cream or custards, and Hollandaise sauces may be made with raw eggs. If the recipe is cooked at some point, this will reduce the exposure to salmonella. Commercially manufactured ice cream, dressings, and eggnog is made with pasteurized eggs and do not increase the risk of salmonella. Sorry, but you should probably resist the raw cookie dough too if it contains raw eggs.

Restaurants should be using pasteurized eggs in any recipe that is made with raw eggs, such as Hollandaise sauce or dressings.

Soft Cheeses

Imported soft cheeses may contain listeria bacteria. It's best to avoid soft cheeses such as Brie, Camembert, Roquefort, Feta, Gorgonzola, and Mexican style cheeses that include Queso Blanco and Queso Fresco unless they clearly state that they are made from pasteurized milk. All soft non-imported cheeses made with pasteurized milk are safe to eat.

Caffeine

Although most studies show that caffeine intake in moderation is permissible, there are others that show that caffeine intake may be related to miscarriages. Encourage mom to avoid caffeine during the first trimester to reduce the likelihood of a miscarriage. As a general rule, caffeine should be limited to fewer than 200 mg per day during pregnancy. That's one 12-ounce cup of coffee. Caffeine is a diuretic, which means it helps eliminate fluids from the body. Don't forget, her favorite soda, chocolate or energy drink probably contains caffiene too.

This can result in water and calcium loss. It is important that your woman is drinking plenty of water, juice, and milk rather than caffeinated beverages. Some research shows that large amounts of caffeine are associated with miscarriage, premature birth, low birth weight, and withdrawal symptoms in infants. The safest thing is to refrain from consuming caffeine.

5

THE NEW DAD CHEATSHEET

"Always plan ahead. It wasn't raining when Noah built the Ark."

— RICHARD CUSHING.

I f you've never been in a delivery room before, you may feel uncertain about your job. Are you supposed to be a cheerleader, a coach, or an unofficial nurse? It's usually a little bit of everything. Your partner will need you at every stage, from the first contractions to the delivery and beyond. You can prepare ahead of time by taking a birthing class with her or talking to other dads about the experience.

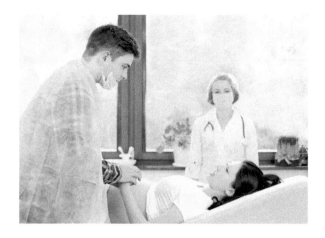

One of the best ways to prepare for childbirth is to accompany your partner to a childbirth education class. Almost all hospitals and birth centers hold classes, and parents-to-be are usually given the option of attending two or three short evening sessions or one long daytime session. You can also choose to go to an offsite class, where the focus may be more on natural childbirth.

Before taking a class, it helps to know a little about childbirth. Here are some of the things you may learn and discuss in a childbirth class:

RECOGNIZING THE ONSET OF TRUE LABOR

Late in pregnancy, many women have painful contractions that may feel like false labor – Braxton Hicks contractions that may start strong but taper off and then stop after a while. Look for these signs, among others, that your partner is experiencing the real deal:

Her water may break, resulting in a trickle or a gush of fluid. When the amniotic sac (also called the bag of waters) breaks, many women spontaneously go into labor shortly after. If not, labor is often induced to minimize the risk of developing an infection. But keep in mind that contractions usually start before her water breaks.

Persistent lower back pain, especially if your partner also complains about a crampy, premenstrual feeling.

Contractions that occur at regular and increasingly shorter intervals and become longer and stronger in intensity.

She passes the mucus plug, which is in the cervix. This isn't necessarily a sign that labor is imminent – it could still be several days away. But at the very least, it indicates that things are moving along.

TIMING THE CONTRACTIONS

Use a timer – for most people, this will be the one on their phone, but anything that will count seconds is fine – to time your partner's contractions in seconds from the beginning of one contraction to the beginning of the next. Count the frequency of contractions in minutes.

If she's having regular painful contractions lasting 30 seconds or more, she's probably in early labor. Your doctor or midwife can help you decide on the phone about when to come in.

As a general rule, if the contractions are five minutes apart or less, last more than 30 seconds, and continue in that pattern for an hour, it's time to go to the hospital. Some situations call for getting to the hospital sooner, so talk to your caregiver ahead of time about what's right for you.

HECK! IT'S TIME FOR HOSPITAL

Don't head to the hospital the minute your partner goes into labor. If she's dilated to only 1 centimeter, chances are they'll send you home or tell her to go for a walk until it's clear she's in labor.

Take a walk, go to the mall or a museum, hit the beach, catch a movie – do anything to help your partner take her mind off the contractions. Though it may not be easy, try not to fixate on the clock. If labor begins at night, help your partner get back to sleep for a few hours.

KNOW WHAT TO EXPECT DURING LABOR

Forget those TV sitcom episodes in which a woman goes into labor and a baby pops out by the second commercial. It sometimes happens that fast, but not usually. For most women, especially first-time mothers, labor is a journey, not an event.

Don't expect labor to be over in just a few hours. Every woman's experience is different, but it's helpful to understand that there are three distinct stages of labor:

FIRST STAGE OF LABOR

The first stage consists of three phases:

Early phase: This phase typically lasts up to 12 hours although it's usually considerably shorter for second and subsequent babies. As labor progresses, the contractions get longer and stronger.

Active phase: Often this phase lasts up to six hours, although it can be a lot shorter. You should be in the hospital or birth center by now or en route. Contractions are much more intense, last about 40 to 60 seconds, and are spaced three to five minutes apart.

Breathing exercises, relaxation techniques, and coaching are all important now. If your partner is having trouble coping or she's not interested in drug-free labor, this is when she might opt for an epidural or other pain relief.

Transition phase: This phase can last anywhere from a few minutes to several hours. It's here that your partner is most likely to swear at you like a truck driver. (Don't take it personally – even women who have coped well up to this point often "lose it" during the transition phase.)

Contractions last 40 to 60 seconds and come two or three minutes apart.

SECOND STAGE OF LABOR

Pushing and birth. The second stage can last from minutes to hours – the average is about an hour for a first-time pregnancy (longer if she's had an epidural) – and ends with a moment that's made up in equal parts of relief and breathtaking beauty: The birth of your baby.

There's a lot to think about during this phase: Do you want to record the birth on video? Will you want to cut the cord? (Be sure to remind your doctor or midwife if you do and be aware that some hospitals don't allow pictures or videos in the birthing room.)

Does your partner want to try to breastfeed immediately after birth? If so, be sure to tell your doctor and nurses so they can help with that as soon as it's safe for your baby to do so.

THIRD STAGE

Delivery of the placenta. It's not over yet! This stage, which begins immediately after the birth of your baby and ends with the delivery of the placenta five to 10 minutes later, is usually anticlimactic but necessary.

Your partner may get a case of chills or feel very shaky during this phase. If that's the case, be ready to offer a warm blanket and to hold your newborn while your partner's regaining her strength.

"WHAT'S MY JOB, ANYWAY?"

Above all, you should ask your partner to talk about what she wants and needs. She'll let you know. It's a good idea to discuss with her what she thinks she'll want from you during labor. It should be your job to make all the arrangements for getting to the hospital. You should also be the one to keep in touch with the rest of the family and screen phone calls while labor is in progress.

Early labor

During the first few hours of labor, your main job is to be a distraction. Ask her if she wants her back or feet rubbed. Put on some music and walk around the room with her. Encourage her to do anything other than lying still and dreading the next contraction.

Active labor

As contractions become stronger and closer together, your role becomes more and more important. If you attended a birthing class, now's the time to put all of those lessons into action. If you didn't go to a class, ask the nurse for tips.

At this point, your main job is to help keep your partner focused. She shouldn't give up, and she shouldn't panic. If she starts acting restless or agitated during a contraction, make eye contact with her and encourage her to take a deep breath. Hold her hand and tell her she's doing great.

But be prepared for the possibility that your encouragement may not be well received at times. One San Francisco doctor recalls a dad whose wife screamed at him to shut up when he told her -- in mid-contraction -- that she was doing great. Between contractions, you will be your partner's caretaker and servant at the same time. If she wants some ice chips, you'll be getting some. Pronto. If she wants a back rub, you'll be rolling up your sleeves and getting to work.

Delivery

This is the big moment, an event you'll remember for the rest of your life. And here's the tough part: You must STAY CALM. Try to save your tears and hysteria until after the baby is born. Your wife needs your support, figuratively and literally. You'll be giving her encouragement with every push, and you may also be supporting her back so she can push comfortably. If you're up to it, you should also take a few moments to watch the actual birth. When you get your first glimpse of your baby's head, you can reassure your partner that she's almost done.

The Aftermath

Men often have two impulses after watching their child being born. First, they cry. Then they grab a camera. As your partner holds your baby for the first time, you'll be firing the flashbulb. After a few good shots, you'll want to put down the camera and pick up your baby. Hold him close and let him study your face.

If your baby goes to a nursery while your partner recovers, go along and keep him company. When he drifts off to sleep, you can make the first round of phone calls to friends and family. And don't forget to check in with your partner, too. If she's awake, she'll want to hear the very latest on the baby's condition. She'll also want to hear how great she was.

Cut The Cord if You Want

Many dads and partners choose to cut their baby's umbilical cord in the first minutes after birth. If you want to cut the cord, don't be shy about reminding your partner's doctor or midwife.

When The Unexpected Happens

You and your wife should already have a detailed birth plan. You should know what kind of interventions she wants or doesn't want, and you should be ready to remind doctors and nurses of her wishes. But once labor starts, you have to be prepared for the unexpected. If the labor isn't going smoothly, your wife might need an intervention that she hadn't signed up for, such as pain medication or even a cesarean section.

If there's a decision to be made, your cool head will be essential in helping her make it. And when your child asks about his birthday, you'll have a story to tell.

TRANSITION WITH BABY FROM HOSPITAL TO HOME

It's time to make your great escape back home with your baby, you may think it's as simple as going from A to B. After all, you've done the drive a fair few times. A couple of days ago, in fact. But oh no. It's not as simple as grab-

and-go. Because once it's time to bring baby home, you ignite the dad-mode of travel. So what can new parents, expect?

Whether your baby comes home from the hospital right away, arrives later (perhaps after a stay in the neonatal intensive care unit), or comes through an adoption agency, the homecoming of your little one is a major event you've probably often imagined. It is a momentous journey that you'll remember forever. Behold my handy guide to bringing your baby home from the hospital in these easy steps.

Discharge and paperwork.

Before you can go, the midwife needs to discharge you. The baby needs a last looking over. And you will probably stand thisclose to the doctor to make sure everything is okay.

Get bub ready to go.

Dress your newborn and gently place them into the capsule (or in your arms if you're using a non-transferable car seat).

Take a picture of bub in a capsule.

Naw... Your little one is so small in that big car seat. And so squishy. Take 15 different pictures, just to make sure you get the right angle.

Realize bub has pooed.

He has pooed all over that super-cute 'going-home' outfit. And, if you're (un)lucky, it's leached through to the car seat too. Take baby out. Retrieve emergency going-home outfit out of the bag and redress bub. Repeat step three.

Stop.

Let every person coo over your newborn as you walk through the ward. Because no one can resist having a sneaky peek at a brand new baby in a capsule. And how can you resist not wanting to share all that royal squishiness with all those new admirers?

Exit the hospital.

Fresh air! Glorious fresh air! This is probably the first time your newborn has been exposed to outdoor air. So naturally, you're going to freak out that their head is cold and frantically pull the nappy bag apart to search for the itty bitty baby beanie.

Put baby into the car seat.

This is usually the time when new parents discover that the whiz-bang car seat they religiously road-tested doesn't click in and out so easily when an actual baby is inside. Try 87 times. Finally, get it.

Once you have bub clipped in and ready to go, expect to check that they are safe and secure another 35 times. This average goes down dramatically with each subsequent child.

Return to hospital.

Because you're pretty sure you left the baby's dummy on the counter. And possibly part of your mind too. Retrieve the dummy. Realize that your partner's pre-baby brain won't be returning anytime soon.

Take more photos of baby in capsule.

#babysfirstdrive #supercuteness #slowdown

Get the trek home.

You're on the road. And in the middle of crazy rush-hour traffic. As bub is now asleep you have nothing to focus on except the dangers all around you. Buses, trucks,

Deliveroo drivers. And naturally, it's your fault (according to mom) for taking this route.

Enter house.

And a brand new wild journey ahead. Sure, the house might look the same as when you left it, but the world will never be the same again after bringing home baby. Buckle up! The car ride home is just the beginning.

SETTLING IN COMFORTABLY AFTER THE TRANSITION

It's okay to be nervous when bringing baby home from the hospital, especially if this is your first child. It's also completely normal to feel uncertain or even overwhelmed as you and your newborn discover sleeping and feeding routines that work best.

However, if overwhelmed feelings worsen or develop into feelings of depression, hopelessness, or despair, contact your healthcare provider right away. There's no shame in doing so. Many parents don't realize that their hormones are likely to continue shifting for months after giving birth, which can also contribute to what may feel like a roller-coaster of emotions.

As you transition from hospital to home, decide how and when you'd like family, friends, and other visitors to stop by. It's perfectly acceptable to ask anyone who was recently under the weather to wait until they're feeling 100% well before coming over to visit you or the baby.

You may also consider asking visitors to wash their hands before helping with or holding your little one since his or her immune system is still very immature and continues to develop after birth before being at full strength.

Most importantly, it's essential to remember to go with the flow during your newborn's first few weeks and months at home – whether you are experiencing motherhood for the first time or you have other children. Your family just got bigger and it may take some time to get back into routines (or even get a full night of sleep!), but these are precious moments that won't last forever and should ultimately be enjoyed.

WHEN TO CALL THE DOCTOR

Your baby's health care provider expects calls from new parents on many topics, including breastfeeding and health concerns (for more on newborn care, visit the Pregnancy & Newborns section). They'd rather have you call than worry about something needlessly.

If you wonder whether you should call the doctor's office, do it, especially if you see something unexpected or different that concerns you. Call if you see any of these signs:

- Rectal temperature of 100.4°F (38°C) or higher (in babies younger than 2 months)
- Symptoms of dehydration (crying without tears, sunken eyes, a depression in the soft spot on baby's head, no wet diapers in 6 to 8 hours)
- A soft spot that bulges when your baby's quiet and upright
- A baby that is difficult to rouse
- Rapid or labored breathing (call 911 if your baby has breathing difficulty and begins turning bluish around the lips or mouth)
- Repeated forceful vomiting or an inability to keep fluids down
- Bloody vomit or stool
- More than eight diarrhea stools in 8 hours.

6

NEW DAD SURVIVAL KIT

"Getting organized is a sign of self-respect."

— GABRIELLE BERNSTEIN

Have you ever heard your dad talk about the day you were born? He may be able to describe the weather or the big story on the television news. Chances are, though, he can't talk about your actual birth. Back then, fathers were often barred from the delivery room. While your mother was pushing, your dad was probably in another room, worrying and looking at his watch.

When you talk to your kids, the story will be different. You'll be able to describe the look on their faces when they entered the world. You'll be able to tell them how you felt watching them being born. And you'll be able to recount their mom's heroism. She did all the hard work, but you were right beside her. And that's pretty heroic, too.

Waiting for the birth of a new baby, and expecting it anytime in the last months of pregnancy is not an easy experience at all. The last few months of pregnancy passed very slow and heavy on both of us; me and my wife.

One day my wife felt some real pain, we hurried to the hospital, the doctor made a quick check and it was a false alarm! The baby was training us on how to respond to the event. He was checking whether we were ready or not? He was testing the speed of our response and all the precautions we were preparing. It was not funny when it happened, but after it passed, we were more mature towards the false alarms!

A few days later, the alarm was not false and that's how my journey to "BECOMING A FATHER" began.

When it's your turn, it's likely to happen when you least expect it. And if you don't get some things in place now, then I'm sorry... you may love neither yourself nor the experience that day.

The word NO

Trust me on this one, after having three kids you need to learn when it comes birthing time to use the word no. Remember you are trying to keep your partner comfortable during the process and she may not want those visitors peaking in. So you have to step in and say no. At times it may not be no but you may need to redirect with, can you come back in 30 minutes as my wife is feeding the baby or resting, etc. If you have a tough time saying no then start practicing once you find out you're having a kid, as there will be some point during the delivery process you will have to say no to someone.

Snacks

Since this is your first time in the hospital awaiting the arrival of your baby then you might notice that sometimes time seems to stand still. While you are doing great at encouraging your partner, your stomach is probably saying "Hey, don't forget about me!". It is important to grab some snacks to help you keep up the energy you will need during labor and then delivery! Pick some great treats high in protein like peanut butter crackers, protein bars, or your favorite candy! Just make sure the smell won't be offensive to your laboring partner. We learned our lessons, that's why we are writing this new dad hospital survival kit

Pain Relievers

While you might be up on your feet and running around making sure your partner is stocked with ice chips, cool cloths, laboring balls, and everything else in between you might just notice that your feet are getting sore. Since you are packing your own bag for the hospital go ahead and throw in some Tylenol or Ibuprofen. Those will come in handy when your back, feet, or head begin to hurt from running around or sleeping on those uncomfortable Hospital couches. No mom wants to hear you complain about pain during this time! Take it from me, I am here to help you out!

Change of clothes

As your mom-to-be is preparing and planning for the new baby to arrive by packing all the essentials that she and your newborn will need sometimes they often over-look dads. To make sure she did not pick out matching outfits, go ahead and pack a couple of days worth of clothes. Comfy clothes to lounge around in are great plus a good outfit to go home in!

Phone Chargers or Battery packs

You know everyone and their mother will be blowing up your phone wanting updates on the progress of your partner and baby. You will be like the paparazzi taking a million pictures of the world's most adorable baby. So for WWIII not to start up in the hospital room, you might want to pack a charger or battery pack. I suggest bringing 2 chargers and a fully charged battery pack. Make sure the battery pack is fully charged as nothing like it being dead when you need it. You will thank us later!

Get your Lady a Present

I am not really sure if this is a thing or not but it is better to be prepared than not. You're probably thinking, "Why do I need to give her a present?". Just do it and thank me later. This present is called a Push Gift and it's your gift of gratitude for delivering your baby. It can be, no, it must be something personal and meaningful. So don't get her favorite candy, please. I got my wife a simple necklace with the baby's initials on it! IF you forget the Hospital gift shops have stepped up their game and grab one last minute if you need to but I do suggest getting her something thoughtful.

Toiletries

Dad, if you are going to be at the hospital for a few days then you are going to need to pack a few toiletries. What to include but not limited to these items; soap, shampoo, deodorant, Poo Pourri spray (you're welcome), body wash, razor, and shaving cream. I am sure you will think of some things you will need also based on your personal preferences. But trust me on this one your queen's senses will be heightened so get some Poo Pourri spray or consider using the public restroom.

Money

Maybe you opted to skip on number two earlier, if so then you will need money for the vending machines. Some hospitals have pay-by-the-hour parking meters so make sure that sucker stays fed. Nothing says congratulations on your new bundle of joy quite like a $200 parking ticket! YIKES!

Instant Coffee

This one is so important on our new dad hospital survival kit that it gets its own slot in this list. I don't know about you but I am a coffee drinker and will need some caffeine while waiting oh so patiently for my newborn to make its appearance! Stay awake and alert while tending to your lady as well! Go ahead and throw in a few others for when that babe is in your arms and your partner is demanding caffeine since she's probably been limited or off caffeine for 9 months! Everyone is happy when mama is happy, right?!

New Dad Shirt

Show off how proud you are of your new addition with a fun new dad shirt! There are tons to choose from and it will probably be better than your old college jersey that has seen better days! Impress your lady with a new shirt!

Entertainment

Even though your main job in the hospital is to help out and assist your partner when needed, there will be some downtime too! She will rest when she can so during that time you will have to entertain yourself. Electronics like our phones, laptops, or even a Nintendo Switch seem to be the easiest and most convenient. Just make sure you don't want to get carried away with the video game or TV show and you start yelling. The other patients just might think you are the one having the baby! Stick to a book, trust me!

Gas Mask

To help lighten the mood and bring a little humor to the room make sure to pack a gas mask. Once your newborn is here and cleaned up, the belly of milk, and all snuggly warm they will poop. Offer to change the diaper but grab the gas mask or dust mask! Being able to bring a little humor to the table as a parent will help you out in the long run. Enjoy the little things! Keep reading for more great things to put in your new dad's hospital survival kit.

Pillow and Blanket

No this is not for your new baby, this is for you! Just like hotels, hospitals are not famous for their soft pillow and blankets. Bring the comforts of home to help you rest better and not look like a walking zombie for the first few days as you adjust to being a dad. Just make sure the pillowcase and blanket are clean as you don't want the hospital staff to see your sweat stains!

Everyone Say Cheese!

One of the most common things to pack but often time gets overlooked due to the fact that technology has infiltrated our beings is a camera! I know we all have cameras on our phones, but I like to pack an extra camera for those special moments as our cameras don't always take great photos in lower light. As a bonus tip, ask a close friend or relative to be the photographer when you plan to have visitors. This way you can focus on your little one and the guests! There is going to be a lot going on and you might forget to snap a picture of some people. Delegate that to them instead, it will make your life easier!

BABY REGISTRY - MUST-HAVE ITEMS

It's fun to imagine all the cute clothes and adorable toys you want to add to your baby registry, but when it comes to knowing exactly what you need, it can seem daunting. But don't' fret! I have compiled a list of must have baby registry items so you won't be caught unprepared when your little one, or ones, arrive.

Baby clothes

- 6-10 onesies
- 6-10 undershirts
- 5-7 one-piece pajamas
- 1-3 sweaters or jackets
- 1-3 rompers or other dress-up outfits
- 6-8 socks or booties
- 1-3 hats (broad-brimmed for summer, soft cap that covers ears for winter)

- No-scratch mittens
- 3-5 pairs of pants
- 4-6 swaddle blankets
- 2 blanket sleepers for a winter baby
- Bunting bag or fleece suit for a winter baby
- Gentle laundry detergent

Diapering

- Diaper pail and liners
- Diaper bag
- Diaper cream
- Unscented baby wipes (causes less irritation)
- Soft washcloths
- 6-10 dozen cloth diapers and 6-8 diaper covers, or 2-3 large boxes of disposable newborn-size diapers

Baby bedding

- 1-3 washable crib mattress pads
- 2-4 fitted crib sheets
- 4-6 soft, light receiving blankets
- 1-2 heavier blankets for colder climates

Nursery

- Crib, cradle or bassinet
- Firm, flat mattress that fits snugly in crib
- Rocking, glider, or arm chair
- Baby monitor
- Nightlight
- Dresser
- Toy basket
- 3-4 learning activity toys
- 3-4 rattles
- 2-3 teethers
- Playmat
- Books
- Doorway jumper
- Soft blocks
- Changing pad
- Changing pad cover
- Clothes hamper.

Bathtime

- Baby bathtub
- Baby soap
- Baby shampoo
- 2-4 soft towels or hooded baby towels
- Soft washcloths (keep apart from diaper washcloths)

Feeding

- 10-16 bottles and nipples, both 4- and 8- ounce
- Pump (if you plan to breastfeed)
- Milk storage bags (if you plan to breastfeed)
- Nursing pads (if you plan to breastfeed)
- Nipple cream (if you plan to breastfeed)
- Nursing pillow (if you plan to breastfeed)
- Bottle brush
- Dishwasher basket for small items
- 4-8 bibs
- Burp cloths
- 2-4 pacifiers
- Formula (if not nursing)

Health

- Baby nail clippers or blunt scissors
- Baby thermometer
- Petroleum jelly and sterile gauze (if you decide to circumcise)
- Infant first aid kit

Baby gear

- Infant or convertible car seat
- Stroller or infant carrier
- Baby swing or bouncer
- Playard with bassinet
- High chair

Keep in mind that each baby's needs are going to be unique, and use this list as a guide rather than a rule. If your baby is coming in the winter, you'll want to get warm clothing right away, but if they're coming in the summer, you can put off the coats and extra blankets for a bit.

There are also a few things that you might be tempted to put on your baby registry, but you can probably skip, such as:

Baby shoes – you can get socks and booties and skip the shoes until baby starts walking.

Crib bumpers – bumpers are a hazard and shouldn't be used.

Drop down crib – drop down cribs aren't manufactured anymore. If you are given a hand-me-down, check to make sure it abides by current safety standards.

Bottle warmer – bottle warmers can be convenient, but they really aren't necessary.

Dressy clothes – babies don't get out to many soirees, so if you don't have an upcoming event in your baby's first few months, just stick with the basics.

TOYS – If there's a specific toy you really want, go ahead and add it to your registry, but don't ask for a lot of toys as people will get you plenty anyway.

Diapers/newborn clothes – while these are important to have (we included them on our checklist), keep in mind that you'll likely get a lot of these items whether or not they're on your baby registry and use your best judgment when asking for them.

7

SETTING UP A NURSERY

"It takes a big heart to shape little minds".

— UNKNOWN

Setting up a nursery is part of the excitement of having a baby on the way. It can be fun and gratifying. However, for someone who has never designed a baby's room, it can be difficult to know where to start and what you actually need.

You can use this comprehensive guide to create a room that will be enjoyable and safe with every essential your child will need for the first year or two of life. Keep reading to learn everything you need to know!

DESIGNING A BABY NURSERY IN 4 STEPS

On the one hand, you may have a ton of ideas in your head on what you want to add to the baby's room. On the other hand, you may not. Use these recommendations to get your baby room design going.

PICK A THEME AND STYLE

An easy way to get started with designing the baby's room is picking a theme or style. You can find inspiration from children's books, cartoons, old baby prints, and novelty fabrics. You may like a Victorian style or prefer a more modern approach.

Take a bit of time to pick your theme and style because you don't want to find a better inspiration a few months down the road.

TIP: If you need inspiration then check out Pinterest. You can find millions of fresh ideas by just typing „nursery" to the search engine.

Selecting a theme and style helps narrow down many of the other choices you will need to make during the design process.

SHOP TEXTILES FIRST

Before you buy paint, you need to find the textiles you want to use in the room. The textiles can include wall hangings, bedding, curtain/shade fabrics, throw rugs, pillows, and furniture upholstery.

Remember, it's easier to find a paint chip that matches fabric than trying to match a particular material to a paint sample.

DECIDE ON YOUR COLOR SCHEME

With your theme in mind, style decided and textiles on hand; now it's time to select your color scheme. The wall color will likely be the most dominant color in the room, so choose it with care. Soothing pastels make the baby's room more restful. You can also draw on lighter colors and make the nursery really stand out.

Another consideration is how often you want to repaint the room. A good paint job can last five to ten years (barring toddler intervention with crayons, paint, and markers). Going with a neutral color will help you paint less often.

Go with one or two accent colors. A child's room often ends up being a jumble of color due to the proliferation of toys, books, and clothing. Limiting your accent colors will help them stand out amidst the chaos.

Which Colors to Pick?

It's said that rooms start to affect us in less than 10 seconds, so it's imperative to pick suitable colors for your nursery. All of them affect us in one way or another. Here you can see the basics of five popular colors.

When you decorate a room for an older child, take his or her temperament into account. For example, if your kid is very calm, you may want to decorate the room with little brighter energizing colors. Usually, it's the other way around though. Calming blue color is the top choice for many parents.

Shades of Blue: Blue is generally considered one of the most soothing colors and is good for intellectual work. It's a good idea to combine it with warmer tones though.

Shades of Green: Green promotes harmony and is good for concentration.

Pink: Pink is a soothing color, but using only pink makes the room feel draining.

White: White is a pure color, but use it too much, and the room may feel cold and unfriendly.

Orange and Yellow: These are two warm colors that are best combined with more soothing tones.

CONSIDER ALSO THE CEILING WHEN SETTING UP A NURSERY

In the first months of life, your infant will spend a lot of time on his or her back, looking up. Make the ceiling part of the decor. Paint the ceiling a soothing color and add a bit of interest with decals. Bring a mural up from the wall to the ceiling. Give the ceiling a starry sky.

Installing a ceiling fan is also a good idea for positive airflow and temperature control. A cold room makes it easier for the baby to sleep and helps to prevent SIDS.

You can find many ceiling fans specially designed for nurseries. However, if you don't want to change it out in a couple of years, a simple white one will do the trick.

FENG SHUI OF A BABY BED

You can treat feng shui as simple teaching on how to make rooms more suitable for us. Two-year-olds can already often tell where they want their beds to be. It's best to trust their instincts. But if you're still looking for a place for a baby crib, then a couple of pointers:

- Don't place the crib directly in front of a window because, according to feng shui, the energy flow is too intense for peaceful sleeping
- Place beds or cribs so that they face the door
- Placing many objects with sharp corners around a baby crib isn't advisable as they can cause scary shadows
- All cribs and most toddler beds already have high headboards, which make kids feel safe.

CREATE A PLACE TO NURSE

Whether you are breastfeeding or using formula, you will want a place set up for feeding the baby.

Do you Need a Nursing Chair?

New parents usually buy a nursing chair (I'm no exception here), but if you're tight on a budget or don't have much free space, then I recommend waiting for a couple of weeks. It may turn out that you don't miss it. For example, our boy preferred lying next to his parents while eating and so the feeding usually happened on a couch or our bed.

If you buy one, then get a comfortable, practical nursing chair with a covering that is easy to clean. Arms on the chair will help with positioning both you and the baby for a comfortable feeding, so it probably will make your life more comfortable. You can also have a table with storage within easy reach of the chair so you can have everything you need on hand.

Nursing chairs may be stationary or ones that glide. You can't lock a traditional rocking chair into place to prevent finger pinching as the child grows older so a glider may be a better option if you wish to buy a moving chair.

Make Your Window Coverings Functional and Beautiful

Long, long time ago in 1999 Nature published a study. It suggested that the absence of a nightly period of full darkness in early childhood may be a risk factor in the development of nearsightedness (myopia). Subsequent studies since show that it probably isn't true. So you can safely continue using your night light. That said, if you live in a city like me, then the incoming light is quite bright, and it can cause sleep problems by reducing the amount of melatonin. Melatonin is a substance in your body that regulates your sleep rhythm.

So there's at least one good reason to install blackout curtains or shades to darken the room for the night. As a bonus, some shades reflect heat so you can keep the room cooler for your baby.

As I've noted before, it's a good idea to buy the window coverings before painting, but install them after the job's done. It's so much easier to paint an empty room.

BABY NURSERY LIGHTING

Give the Room Multiple Lighting Options When Setting up a Nursery

Your baby's room should have multiple lighting options. As I've explained before (sorry for repeating myself), exposing your little to bright light before sleeping may cause sleeping problems.

If the room has an overhead lighting fixture, you can install a dimmer switch on it. This will allow you to adjust the light as needed.

Nighttime feedings are more comfortable if you have a second lamp next to the nursing chair. Many lamps have a dimmer switch, so you are able to adjust the light level on the second lamp. This lamp can also serve as a lamp for story time. If you have a floor lamp, then it's a good idea to remove it after your baby starts to crawl because they are easily knocked over.

Nigh Lights

Nightlights are safe to use and can comfort your older kid if he or she is afraid of the dark. At the floor level, they can be useful for safety reasons- you can see enough to avoid tripping on anything.

I haven't yet bought one for my nursery because I want that my all my kids to get used to sleeping in the dark. Thanks to the baby monitor, I don't have a need to go into the nursery while he's sleeping.

SANITATION - BUT DON'T OVERDO IT

Fear of germs or germophobia seems to be a big issue among new parents but try to get over it. Our bodies carry approximately as many bacteria as we have human cells and what's important is the balance. If your baby is exposed to too few bacteria, it may actually be harmful to his or her. For example, the risk of allergies and some chronic diseases rises.

Keep the nursery clean, but use pure water. You rarely need harsh chemicals to clean the room.

Suggestions:

- Select your furniture with easy cleaning in mind
- All textiles should be washable
- Create a place to store cleaning supplies so you can clean up messes without leaving the room
- Know where you are going to dispose of diapers and store soiled clothing.

PART II

NOW A DAD – GUIDE TO BONDING BEST

Yahoo! You have been waiting 9 months for this, and here it is! Your new baby is finally here! Now what do you do? You can scarcely imagine that you have brought this new life into the world. You want the best for your newborn! You will be responsible for influencing this new soul that you have produced. That's a tremendous responsibility! Everything begins with the bonding that you create with your baby.

WHY DOES IT MATTER ANYWAY?

A growing body of research has shown that when dads spend time with their newborns and begin developing a strong relationship with them from the very beginning, they reap a number of benefits.

A child's physical and mental development is significantly boosted when his dad has played with him from the start, compared to children whose fathers took a more hands-off approach.

Fathers experience less stress and increased confidence when they have their own special time with their newborns.

Strong father-child bonds can help counter issues such as depression later on in life.

Men who report that they had a good relationship with their fathers during childhood were found to be better equipped to handle stress.

Children who experienced close interactions with their fathers from an early age tend to be more successful academically, have better relationships with their peers and be less likely to get involved with crime or abuse drugs and alcohol.

8

PLAYMATE - GROWING A BOND

"When she wakes up in the morning, she gets all excited when she sees or hears me. You can't buy that type of feeling."

— VETERAN DAD

Of all the powerful roles in humanity, a father teaching his baby to play has got to be the coolest. Playing, your baby's main job teaches him how to laugh and take risks. It develops his motor skills and speeds the development of his brain and nervous system. Very serious stuff.

As a father, you're designed to be his perfect playmate. Flight lessons, peek-a-boo, and wrestling all come naturally. Furthermore, playing is bonding at its finest. Dads elicit the most radiant smiles and infectious belly laughs, sometimes with just a wink.

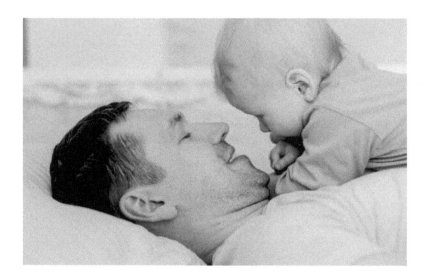

There's a time I saw a first-time father seeking advice on Reddit; saying he had a daughter who had just turned 3 months old. So, he took 2 months off work to spend time with her and the wife after a little rough birth experience that led the baby to NICU and put his wife in ICU.

Fast forward, he said "I've read all the books, give baths, bottle feed(my wife did breastfeed for a while), try and play games(she is not very active yet, at least with her hands), change diapers. I do everything I possibly can to be involved and helpful..."

"But at the end of it, my baby seems very indifferent towards me, doesn't smile too much at me, but lights up with her mom, when she wakes up from a nap and I go and comfort her, she starts screaming but if her mom comes up... she sorta sighs and calms down WITH JUST SEEING her... and the worst part is when I do try and put her to sleep she most likely will fuss unless I am feeding her and she falls asleep at the bottle... she doesn't look at me when I am holding her a majority of the time, but she stares at my wife whenever she is holding her and my wife doesn't have to do much to get her to fall asleep in her arms..."

"I on the other hand have to jump through hoops and fussing to put her to sleep... My wife is a great mom, but I just feel like so much effort is wasted... simply because my wife's best friends also had a baby and her husband doesn't do anything with the child, and the baby obviously fusses when he is with him... so if the results are the same, I sometimes feel I shouldn't try as hard..." "I just wish my daughter would look at me for comfort like she does my wife." - He said.

My suggestion could've been "play harder, new daddy!" Sometimes, the bond is instant; parents fall in love the moment they set eyes on their little "bundle of joy." Other times, bonding with the baby takes longer. The same can be said for the babies; they may (or may not) feel connected to you immediately.

In fact, studies have found that about 20% of new parents feel no real emotional attachment to their newborn in the hours after delivery. Sometimes, it takes weeks or even months to feel that attachment. If you haven't begun bonding with your baby (or vice versa), don't feel anxious or guilty - it should come with time.

Think about it this way; have you ever had a cold that lasts an entire month? Your condition becomes the norm. "Healthy" no longer seems possible. Well, then it's just the same damn scenario.

The important thing to realize is that it doesn't make you a bad parent and, thankfully, there are several things you can do to encourage and improve your burgeoning relationship with your baby.

GUIDELINES FOR PLAYING

While playing with babies comes naturally to dads, there are a few things to keep in mind:

Short Field of Vision at First

For the first couple of weeks, a baby's vision is fuzzy and he'll fixate on things that are about a foot from his eyes. Place a picture or toy with highly contrasting colors in his line of sight to catch his attention, and then move it back and forth slowly so he can track it.

Her Favorite Mug - Yours

She'll focus on your face and recognizes it in about one month. While she likes mom's face too, your whiskers make yours more interesting. For some reason, at around six months, babies like to grab dad's nose and try to pull it off.

Stop When She's Had Enough

She may be finished before you are, and it's important to recognize the signs before you irritate her. If she turns her face away, arches her back, or whimpers when you expect her to be having fun, assume she's worn out or overstimulated and it's time to quit.

Be Careful He Doesn't Get Scared

Getting scared will not just trigger crying; remember all those neurons firing for the first time? You want your baby wired to trust you and his new environment and not grow up anxious. Be gentle and careful about situations—sudden loud noises, people getting too close or picking him up roughly—that may frighten him.

Nurture an Adventurous Spirit

Notice when he's reaching out for something and encourage his exploration. Let him take his time. Let him try for something just beyond his reach. Before you do something for him, let him try to do it himself. Encourage, don't frustrate.

Improvise

Put your creative stamp on playing with your baby; build your repertoire of games that only he (and you) know. Opportunities abound; make your sock into a puppet that sings to him. Dip his toe in ice cream and give him a taste. Blow raspberries on his tummy, stopping and starting a couple of times until he's bouncing with anticipation, then cut loose with a big one.

Just You and Him – Anything Goes

There's no one else around? It's time for ELVIS! Or whatever you like. Got a comedy act buried deep? Drag it out. No matter how bad you truly are, she'll think you're the best.

IT'S A DIRTY JOB AND IT'S DAD'S - GAMES TO PLAY

Here are things to do with your baby from birth through six months. Try them, see what works, and then come up with your own. Getting in even five minutes of play each day is a good start.

0 TO 2 MONTHS

There's always something you can do to engage your baby. Here are some ideas to get you going:

Monkey See, Monkey Do

She might mimic you sticking your tongue out, even as a newborn. As she grows, she may mimic your other facial expressions and cooing sounds, too. Start early: hold her face-to-face, smile, open your mouth and slowly stick out your tongue. Repeat.

Airplane

Hold your baby firmly with both hands—one under her bottom and the other cupped on the back of her head. Lift her in the air and let her "fly" around slowly and gently. Always firmly support her head.

Pull-Ups

Put his face up in your lap, and place one finger in each of his hands so he grabs on. Then pull him up a little, let him down, and repeat.

Baby Calisthenics

With your baby on her back, gently pull her legs up to you and then side to side. Up, out, down, back, reverse. Do the same with her arms.

Walking at One Month

Their walking reflex is very cool. Using both hands to hold him, stand him on the bed and lean him forward. He'll slowly raise one foot as if taking a step and if you move him forward, he'll take another.

Record Your Babbler

When he starts cooing and babbling away, grab your phone, load a voice recorder app, and hit "record." Then play it back to him and watch the fascination in his eyes and the smile on his face. Do the same with his fussing, and he'll stop to take in this new distraction. Keep the recording; it'll be a special memory.

2 TO 4 MONTHS

Your baby will become more active at two to four months, smiling and starting to coo and babble away, and responding more during playtime. She'll love having fun with you, especially when you smile and talk to her. The possibility for games increases; examples include:

Mattress Trampoline

Lay your baby on her back on the bed. Push down on the mattress so that she bounces a little bit. Go slowly and gently so she enjoys it and doesn't get anxious or upset. Remember, she's still learning to trust you, so don't ramp up the action to a level your child isn't yet comfortable with.

Kick Boxing

With your baby lying on his back, put the palms of your hands up so they are nearly touching the soles of his feet. Gently push his foot with your hand, switching back and forth between right and left. Soon, you'll do nothing but hold your hands there and your baby will kick them in the same right to left pattern you initiate.

Baby Acrobatics

Sit on the ground with your baby facing you in your lap. Get a firm grip around his midsection and rollback, holding him up in the air while you say "wheee!" If he loves it—and, there's a good chance he will—you'll be priming him for past-times that will terrify you later in life.

Lots of Belly Time

Since we put our babies to sleep on their backs, they have few opportunities to develop upper body strength by lifting their heads and pushing themselves up with their hands. So give him plenty of belly time while playing, and he'll be the fastest crawler in his Mommy & Me group.

4 TO 6 MONTHS

Your baby is quickly becoming bigger, stronger, more active, and responsive. This opens up a whole new range of possibilities. Babies love to be cheered on at this age, so don't hold back.

Peek-a-Boo

Always a favorite. Put your hands in front of your face for a few moments, then jerk them away and say "peek-a-boo!" Repeat about five times, then put her hands over her eyes and show her how to do it. Over time, she'll catch on and after a month or so you'll be peek-a-booing back and forth with her giggling away.

Her First Song

When she's cooing or babbling, take her hand and place the back of it over her mouth to cork her briefly, then lift it and repeat. The result will be bah-bah-bah, which she'll find fascinating as well as a new trick to enthrall her adoring audience (Mom, Grandma).

Rock 'n' Roll

He'll love this one, though mom may not. Raid the kitchen for wooden spoons and a few pots and use them to make some serious music. Put a spoon in his chubby little hand and show him how to bang a pot like a drum, then cut him loose to bang away on his own. As he flails away, make sure he doesn't inadvertently bang his head or yours.

Hide and Seek

Take something your baby is playing with and hide it inside or underneath something bigger. If it's a cloth book, put it underneath a light blanket. If it's a block, put it inside a plastic bowl. Show him where it is and then hide it again until he finds it himself.

Crawler In Training

Put him on his belly, sideways over a towel. Grab both towel ends in one hand and lift him up a few inches, supporting him with your other hand. Get him on his hands and knees, and start moving his arms and legs one at a time in a crawling motion. While this maneuver may not actually teach him to crawl, he'll find it interesting and maybe even fun—it can't hurt.

LEVEL YOUR GAME UP

Skin to Skin Contact

It is one of the most gorgeous ways to bond with your baby… and it's not just for mums!

When you hold your baby next to your warm skin, baby can hear your heartbeat, snuggle into your chest (whether hairy or not for dads!), and smell your scent.

Babies prefer the real smell of you, so don't go too heavy on the deodorant on perfumes. Skin-to-skin contact can be done anytime; watching the TV, reading, listen to music, dancing to music.

Every time you hold a baby like this we are drawn to look at them and them to look up into our faces. This promotes lifelong bonding and encourages the release of huge amounts of the love hormone, oxytocin.

The other thing skin-to-skin contact does is reduces stress hormone and helps babies to drift off into la-la land and sleep well. Now if that isn't a good excuse to promote it, I don't know what is.

Get Out And About

It's important to try and get out of the house, to the park, the shops, or the library.

The outside world is great for giving you things to talk about with your baby, whether it's the ducks in the park, the cars in the street, or the fruit and veg at the supermarket.

Try and stop to get face-to-face with your baby as you stroll. This will let you see what's grabbing their attention more easily, and you can talk about that.

On your travels, keep an eye out for things that are happening in your community. There might be a group out there that's calling for you and your skills.

For example, in Blackpool, there is a community shed for dads to come along and create things for their kids.

So if you've spent years tinkering with bikes, cars, or computers, that practice making things could come in handy! Find as many ways to speak to your baby as you can. It's important to start talking to babies as early as you can.

This gets babies used to hearing your voice and responding, even before they can form words. And think about it, before baby can complain, it's the ideal time to practice your "dad jokes"!

It's great to be daft with your baby. If you're smiling and happy, chances are you'll get a smile out of them, even if the jokes themselves don't get them chuckling (yet...).

It's always good to try and speak to babies face-to-face and to look for signs that they're trying to communicate.

Encourage them to babble (that's when they make noises like they're doing baby speak) by leaving them time to respond after you speak to them. Think of it like tennis, waiting for a return every time you talk.

Become Number One Storyteller

Storytelling is a role that dads can really revel in. Try having a bit of 'story time' each day when you're with your baby. Not only will it help in creating a strong bond with you, but also a great way to help your child learn language.

You can tell stories you know, or make up stories on the spot. Be as daft as you want, make up whatever characters you like.

Or, you could read stories out from a book. But you don't need to read books word for word. In fact, it's better if you can point out pictures, put on voices and make noises.

In Blackpool, dads are taking part in woodwork classes, creating figures based on the stories they tell to their children. That way they have toys that bring their stories to life. So, if you're handy with making things, why not have a go at making some characters yourself? You don't have to use wood, just make sure it's a safe material, and don't let your baby try to eat the figures!

Make Connections With Other Dads

Chances are, a lot of new dads and soon-to-be dads have similar hopes and fears to you.

By meeting other dads, you'll be able to share your experiences and help each other out. Once you're both laughing at the things that worry you, they're bound to lose their edge.

A good way to meet other dads is to try and make it out to classes and groups with your partner.

You might feel a bit uncomfortable striking up conversations with the other guys in waiting rooms, but every man you see in these places is in a similar boat. They might need a 'dad buddy' to help them make sense of it all too.

If you are struggling and you're not sure who to speak with, then there are places online that offer help too.

9

FEEDING YOUR TOT

"The way to a man's heart is through his stomach"

— IAN SOMERHALDER

The old days of Mom being the caregiver and Dad's interaction with Baby limited to "Wave to Daddy, honey" is over. Today, lots of dads are involved in baby care and child-rearing in ways that would make our grandfathers shudder. More and more fathers are doing more and more to share parenting with mothers. Even breastfeeding moms are making it possible for dads to bottle feed baby—may be out of necessity, maybe to encourage a father-child bond, maybe to improve their bond with Dad.

Yet there are still few resources available to help new dads learn what to do for and with their infant. Here, I share wih you a simple guide:

FINDING THE DAMN BOTTLE

Buying the right bottle is the same as shopping for any of the million other things you need but would prefer not to have to shell out for. Start with the cheaper bottles from Coles or Woolworths and then get progressively more expensive as your baby decides that you being a tight-arse is not in their best interests.

Bottles from the supermarkets can cost as little as $10. This is a great thing if your baby takes to them. Otherwise, like me, you could find yourself shelling out upwards of $50 for fancy-pants soft silicone bottles which are meant to mimic the feel of the breast (this is not as exciting as it sounds).

Fabulous for baby but not ideal for you. You will lose them and have a minor heart attack every time you have to pay for another.

PREPARING THE BOTTLE

Breastmilk Preparation:

Frozen breastmilk can be thawed overnight in the fridge, or by placing the bag under warm running water. Gradual warming is key, so if you want to thaw breast milk faster, use something like the Dr. Brown's MilkSpa that safely warms breast milk without removing important nutrients. Before putting the milk in the bottle, make sure it's clean by giving it a quick wash (as well as your hands).

Formula Preparation:

Whether you will be using formula exclusively or supplementing, there are a few tricks to making the most out of each bottle.

Wash the bottle, parts, and your hands before mixing. Follow the formula maker instructions for mixing guidelines but make sure to measure precisely, as too much powder can cause an upset stomach for your little one. Mix thoroughly, ensuring there are no clumps that can get stuck in the nipple. Remember that formula stays good for two hours at room temp or 24 hours if refrigerated.

GETTING THE TEMP RIGHT

No baby likes cold milk. Even in summer, room temperature is better than cold. Fussy little ...

Anyway, you have options. Automatic drivers will prefer the bottle warmer. Milk in the bottle, bottle in warmer, press the button and wait for the beep – unless you don't want to spend the $80+ it will cost for a half-decent warmer. Or if like my son's, your bottle is silicone, it'll warm up as quickly as a 1978 BMW 3 Series. Fun times.

Your other option is to plonk the bottle in a bowl of warm water. This takes a while to heat but it's predictable and works on all types of bottles. And it's free.

Don't forget to swirl the milk to get rid of hot spots. If the milk is too hot, but will still try to drink it but will likely come off after every sip. Don't force it. Fridge for a few minutes, or a splash of cold pre-boiled water, will do the job.

PUTTING ON THE SHOW

Relax And Be Confident

Baby won't know nervousness when she feels it, but she will sense that something is not right. If you aren't relaxed, neither will she be. If she isn't relaxed she won't eat well, or if she does eat, it won't stay down. If you are nervous, take some deep breaths, stretch your back, shake out your hands, and look at that little bundle—she is depending on you. You got this!

Act as if it is: even if you aren't feeling 100% confident in your bottle-feeding skills, act as if you were. Eventually, the act becomes the reality.

Get Comfortable

Feeding a baby is not something that can be rushed. You can't do it while you are on the go or in a quick minute between other tasks. Kick-off your shoes and find a comfortable seat; you'll be there for about half an hour. The more comfortable you and Baby are, the better he will eat. Make feeding time a ritual and you and your baby will enjoy it better.

Bottle feeding baby might just give you an excuse to hang on to that recliner your mother-in-law has been complaining about.

Find The Right Position

The milk or formula flows much faster from the bottle than it does from the breast. To keep Baby from choking or having to gulp, hold her in a more upright position than breastfeeding mom does—more of a 45-degree incline, rather than 90 degrees sitting up or lying flat on her back. It can be difficult to find the right position, but you'll keep trying because you want the best for Baby.

It will take some practice to find what's most comfortable for you, and what works best for your baby.

Feeling The Flow

Flow is a tricky thing. Different teats have different flows and while you will obviously start with the lowest flow when your baby is a newborn, knowing when to move up to a faster one is tricky and messy. Sorry, but it's just trial and error here.

It is likely that bub will look like a rubbish contestant in an eating competition for a while. It all goes roughly towards the mouth, some of it in, some of it out, and then some that went in comes out again. Don't wear your crisp white business shirt from Mr. Lauren while you do this! Milk is nowhere near as white as you think it is.

Here's a trick anyway - Wait for the latch

Whether you start bottle feeding after the baby has got the hang of nursing with mom, or immediately after he's born, be sure to make sure that your baby's lips are sealed around the nipple of the bottle. Your baby has limited to no experience sucking. First, check if the nipple of the bottle is on the tongue, not under it. You'll have to help by to gently pushing his lower lip up to the nipple.

Have patience as both of you are learning a new skill.

Look At Your Baby

According to some studies, babies can recognize faces after only a few days. Be sure to look at and engage with your baby as you feed him. You can sing or talk to him, too. These are the first days, weeks, and months of a lifetime relationship. The more you and Baby get to know one another, the more comfortable both of you will be. This is the start of you being his go-to guy.

Be aware, though, intense eye contact may distract your baby from the act of nursing.

Take Off Your Shirt Papa

Skin-to-skin contact has amazing health benefits for your baby, so strip off that shirt. After spending months near mom's heart, babies benefit from skin-to-skin contact in several ways. Their breathing and heart rate stabilize by being near yours; their body begins to learn to regulate their internal temperature, and they are generally happier. If the air is cool, cover both of you with a blanket. As a plus, not wearing a shirt will eliminate stains on that shirt.

Some babies prefer to be swaddled, that is, wrapped tightly in their blankies. Even when swaddling, you can accomplish skin-to-skin contact with your child's head.

Switch Arms

Burping time is a good time to switch arms. When you are feeding Baby, you'll be holding him with one arm and holding the bottle with the other. Switching baby from one arm to the other mimics the breastfeeding mom and provides both you and baby some relief from staying in the same position. Changing arms eases pressure on your back and Baby's neck and back. It also gives Baby a new perspective on the world and allows you to enjoy another view of that precious face.

You may find that you are more comfortable holding a baby on one side. Try to learn to be comfortable on both sides, as the baby should switch from time to time.

Finally: Fall in Love

Probably the most important tip for feeding your baby is to just do it. Bottle feeding your child provides a definite huge benefit, one that you won't get from changing diapers and taking out the trash.

The best part about bottle feeding your baby is that you have to opportunity for uninterrupted one-on-one time with your new love. Take this time to fall deeply in love with that little person. Touch those little toes, feel him breathe along with you, kiss his little forehead. Love him like you'll never love another.

Bottle feeding—more than any other action Dad can take in the first year—creates a bond between Daddy and Baby. Dads who take an active role in the early years of their kids' lives are more involved in the later years. There's no better way to get involved than by bottle feeding. You are creating a lifelong bond.

You'll need this bond when he becomes a teenager.

BURPING IT UP!

Do you know how good it feels to burp sometimes? Sometimes babies need the same kind of relief. And helping them burp can be a good Dad job.

But first. Burping is a little over-rated. People sometimes act like parents have to make sure their babies burp at absolutely every feeding.

Not really.

In cultures where babies are carried upright all the time, in slings or on their mother's back, parents "burping their babies" is unheard of. Babies who are carried a lot often just burp when they need to on their own. So, carry your baby around against your shoulder after a feeding and see what happens.

If she's fallen asleep don't feel you have to wake her up to burp her. Leave her be.

On the other hand, there are situations where burping might not be a bad idea:

If the baby had been crying for a while before feeding, she may have swallowed air while crying and need help in bringing it up.

If you are feeding your baby with a bottle, she might swallow air if her lips didn't make a good seal around the bottle nipple.

If you or your partner think the baby needs burping. A lot of early parenting is guesswork. You try things and see if it helps. If you think your baby might be swallowing air, or might need to burp, go for it. Believe us, there are no support groups for adults who were burped too often as babies.

Here are three different ways to burp... the baby.

The Classic.

Try putting him high up on your shoulder so that your shoulder presses just below his tiny ribcage, then gently pat his back. Oh, and, um, put receiving blanket or burp pad on your shoulder first. Trust us on this one!

Sit-down burping.

Drape the baby across your lap, which puts a little pressure on his tummy, and pat his back gently. You might have to experiment a bit to find a position that feels right.

The "folding" technique sometimes works with small babies. Hold him in a sitting position, with one hand supporting his chin (so his head doesn't flop forward) then gently bend him forward a little bit, chest toward knees. Then straighten him up again. Repeat a couple more times.

No need to push it. If you don't hear a satisfying belch after a minute or two, chances are there's no burp to come up. However, if your baby starts to grimace or wiggle around as though he's uncomfortable when you lay him down, it's worth giving it another try.

Spitting up.

Lots of babies spit up small amounts of swallowed milk after some feedings. Some do it after just about every feeding. It's normal and although people have looked for ways to prevent it, there is no proven solution. If your baby is a spitter-upper - you'll know - just always keep a receiving blanket over your shoulder if you're holding the baby right after feeding. Oh and buy laundry detergent when it's on sale. You'll need extra.

10

BATHING AND DRESSING A NEWBORN

"Baby, baby, baby oooh. Like baby, baby, baby nooo"

— JUSTIN BIEBER

When it comes to newborn bath time, the more hands, the better — in other words, make the first few baths a team effort. Set up beforehand, and do it when you're feeling calm. (Breathe. In...out...in. Good.) Commit to letting voicemail pick up any calls — for this project, all your attention should be on baby.

Here's what you need for a successful bath time:

Washing station

Whether you bathe baby in a sink lined with a soft surface or a plastic tub with a sling placed in the real bath, your setup should be steady and there shouldn't be anything hard or sharp for baby to accidentally knock against. Position baby's head away from the faucet (and use a soft faucet cover, if you have one).

Warm room

Keep the temperature raised so it's not a shock to baby's system when she comes out of the bath. Babies have a hard time regulating their core temperature, so they shouldn't be chilled for too long.

Water

Fill the tub about three inches with water a little bit warmer than lukewarm. Submerge your entire hand and wrist to check the temperature. The water shouldn't be running while baby is in the tub, because the depth could quickly become dangerous, or the water temperature could change and become too hot. (Tip: Turn your water heater down to 120 degrees to avoid accidental scalding.)

Plastic pitcher or cup

Use this to pour water over baby and rinse her off. (This is safer and less scary for babies than the gush of water coming from a faucet.) Or squeeze a washcloth soaked in water over baby's head to rinse.

Soap

Though some moms prefer to use only water on their newborns, the sweat and dead skin that accumulate on baby can produce an odor that makes soap pretty welcome. Go easy on the amount, though, because too much can dry out baby's skin. Look for a mild, tear-free cleanser that can be used for both baby's body and hair. (Even tear-free soap should be kept away from baby's eyes and face, though.) Some parents prefer all-natural baby wash, so that's good too. Bottles that open with one hand or use a lockable pumping mechanism are best, because they allow you to keep that one necessary hand on baby at all times. If baby has a hard time with the washcloth, just put soap on your hands and clean him that way.

Washcloths

Designate a certain color or pattern used specifically for bath time — you wouldn't want to confuse them with your diaper cloths!

Any special treatments

Diaper cream, cradle cap treatment, or any other remedies your doctor has recommended should be within reach.

Timing

Pay attention to baby's mood after bath time, and use it to your advantage. If he's energetic and ready to play, bathe during the day. If he seems more mellow, make it a pre-bedtime activity.

STEP BY STEP PROCEDURE:

Start by soaking baby a little. Always keep one hand on baby, and remember that infants are especially slippery when wet. If baby needs cradle cap treatment, put this on first, then come back to rinse after you've washed the rest of his body.

Otherwise, start from the top and work your way down. Wash the face first, cleaning one area at a time — it can be scary for infants to have their entire face covered with a washcloth. As you move down the body, thoroughly wash inside all the folds (including under the arms, in the neck and the genital area).

Sweat and skin can get stuck in those areas and fester, causing nasty rashes, so it's important to keep them as clean and dry as possible. Save baby's dirtiest parts (aka the diaper area) for last. Then, move back up and wash baby's hair.

Since infants lose most of their heat through their heads, this should be your very last move. If the water is still warm you can engage in a little playtime, but resist the urge to splash for too long — as the water chills, baby will quickly get cold.

There's no need to bathe more than every few days. Since babies' skin is so dry it can dehydrate quickly, so it's actually best not to wash daily. Some parents even get by with as little as once a week. As one doctor put it, "When they start to smell funny, you know it's time for a bath."

BATH-SIDE SETUP:

Towels

Keep a few towels on hand — one to carefully dry out all the little folds, and then another one fresh out of the dryer (but not too hot) to wrap baby up in. (Roll it up to keep in the warmth.) Hooded towels are also a good buy.

- Clean diaper

- Clean clothes
- Blanket
- Lotion

Some babies love lotion massages after bath time. Remember, though — flaking skin isn't necessarily dry. Babies accumulate dead skin that needs to come off.

- Hairbrush or comb
- For those babies blessed with tresses.

Note: Until the cord stump falls off (about 7 to 9 days) and the circumcision is healed, baby should only have sponge baths. Wrap baby in a towel to keep him warm, then pull out one limb at a time to wash with a sponge and warm water. The cord stump can get infected, so it should always be kept clean and dry. If it seems dirty or sticky, wash it with soap and water and then dry well using a clean cloth.

DRESS AND UNDRESS A BABY

Dressing and undressing your baby is wonderful face-to-face time that you can spend interacting with each other. Talking to your baby calmly can help keep her relaxed during the process. When putting clothes on or taking clothes off your baby, always make sure to:

Handle your baby carefully and gently. Work slowly and tell him what you're doing. As you dress and undress your baby more often, you'll become more comfortable and the process will go more smoothly.

Remove clothes with care. When removing any item of clothing, work to carefully loosen it. Be careful to not twist your baby or move too quickly to avoid overextending his arms or legs or putting him into any uncomfortable positions.

Choose the correct size clothes. You don't want to dress your baby in clothes that are too short or too tight. The neck of any shirt should be comfortable and the legs should be long enough so that he can extend his legs.

Make sure your baby's clothes are safe. If your baby's clothes have buttons or decorations, make sure they are securely stitched so that she cannot remove them.

Choose layers when dressing your little one. Dressing newborns in layers is a great way to make sure that they are warm and comfortable. Layers can be easily added or removed depending on the temperature and your baby's comfort level. A good rule of thumb: Dress your baby in as many layers as you are wearing, with perhaps one more on hand to add on in case your baby gets cold.

Place your baby on a safe, flat surface. Lay a blanket down to cushion the surface.

HOW TO DRESS A BABY

When putting a shirt over your baby's head, gather the entire shirt like an accordion up to the neck. Holding the opening of the neck, carefully place the shirt over your baby's head and slowly pull the shirt over her body.

Gather the sleeves up to the cuff and put your baby's hand through the opening. Carefully work the sleeve up the rest of her arm.

When putting on pants, start at your baby's feet and gradually work the outfit up her body.

If you need to fasten the back of an outfit, gently turn your baby on to her tummy or sit her up with support.

HOW TO UNDRESS A BABY

Begin at your baby's head and carefully loosen and slide the outfit down over the body.

Be sure to support your baby's head and body with one hand as you lift him to reposition clothes. Remember to avoid twisting or jerking any of your baby's limbs at any time.

Carefully unsnap each snap and loosen or rearrange the item until it can be easily removed. For instance, use two hands to remove the socks gently rather than pulling them off the feet.

If you need to turn your baby on his side, be sure to support his body weight.

To get a bodysuit or shirt off of your little one, carefully lift her up off the table, and support her head and body. Slowly remove sleeves, working down toward the wrist.

11

BECOMING A DIAPER-CHANGING MACHINE

"Politicians and diapers must be changed often, and for the same reason."

— MARK TWAIN

Diaper changing is not for the faint of heart. I say this because I've seen grown men gag and throw up at the sight of baby poop. Some cringe with just the smell of the baby excrements. Well, this chapter is a call to you, first-time dad, to suck it up and face the truth. Your baby will poop, and diapers need to be changed.

You can rely on your partner or the nanny, but the skill comes in handy when you're alone with your little one. Moreover, by doing this task, you lighten the load for mom. So give your lady a break and take on this challenge.

This is bonding time with your baby. Of course, the poop can be a turn-off but spending quality time knows no limitations. The first few tries will still make you squeamish. However, as you change more nappies, the easier it becomes.

Furthermore, you will find your own technique and the best way to master your new art. I've done it and I'm sure all dads out there can do it as well. It's one activity every dad should experience. When you experience changing your baby's nappies, you'll never look at baby poop the same way again.

Before practically changing those nappies, however, there are a few things that your new daddy brain needs to know.

DIFFERENT KINDS OF BABY POOP

Let's first talk about the different kinds of poop. I bring this up because in the hospital it seems like the doctors and nurses are very interested/concerned in how many times your newborn has pooped and peed. They are interested and/or concerned for good reason since all this indicates if everything is working internally.

Poop from newborns for the first few days will look like a combination of motor oil and caramel. It is very sticky. This kind of poop is called meconium. It looks this way because it is made up of the stuff (intestinal epithelial cells, lanugo, mucus, amniotic fluid, bile, and water) your baby ingested while in utero. You will find that meconium is hard to clean off your baby's bum, but the good news is that it does not smell bad.

The second kind of poop you will see from your newborn will be what is called transitional poop. This poop happens usually between 2 and 4 days old. It's lighter in color than meconium (kind of army green and less sticky). Transitional poop is a sign that your newborn is beginning to digest early breast milk or formula and that everything is okay with his intestinal tract. This poop will last for the first week of life.

After transitional poop comes breastfed poop. This kind of poop often looks like Dijon mustard (yellow and/or greenish) with cottage cheese mixed in. It also may be dotted with seed-like flecks. For the benefit of fathers who struggle with poopy diapers this kind of poop does not smell all that bad.

If your baby is not breastfed then he will be formula fed which means his poop will look different. Formula-fed or bottle-fed poop is brown with a thick and creamy consistency. If the formula you give your newborn is iron-fortified then his poop will be dark brown or dark green.

When baby poop starts to get smelly is when you start feeding your baby solid foods like infant cereal, pureed bananas, and stuff like that. This kind of poop is called solid-food poop. It's brown or dark brown and thicker than peanut butter, but still mushy.

LET'S TAKE THE STINK OUT!

Step 1: Have everything you need within reach.

I usually open up the new diaper ready for use. My wife has a changing bag with everything needed in it. This beats having to fumble with stuff every time we need to change our baby's diaper. This also ensures that everything we need is available.

Here are the things that you need: changing pad, new diaper, plastic bag for the soiled diaper, cotton or gauze pad for wiping the baby, baby wipes (don't use wipes with alcohol, they can irritate your baby's skin), anti-rash cream, petroleum jelly.

Step 2: Wash your hands and sanitize.

You should also remove your ring, bracelets, or any accessories that may scrape your child's skin. It is also a good idea to warm your hands first before you touch your baby. Cold hands can be uncomfortable for them.

Step 3: Place your baby on the changing table or bed.

Note: Changing tables have straps to secure your baby so use them. For those who do have changing tables, your bed or any flat surface is good enough. Just make sure you put a blanket or towel underneath your baby to make it comfortable. Likewise, ensure that there is ample space for the baby.

Step 4: Unstrap & Fold.

Unstrap the dirty diaper and fold the flaps so it does not stick to your baby's skin. Some diapers don't use sticky tape but it is still a good idea to fold it back.

Step 5: Fold-down the top part of the dirty diaper.

This will expose the baby to poop. Some poop may still be sticking to your baby's skin so scoop them off with the top part of the used diaper or you can use a damp cotton/

cloth to do this. If the skin is sensitive, you can use sterile gauze. Make sure you clean the whole area.

Note: To avoid infections, use a top to bottom motion when cleaning the genital area - especially when the baby is a girl. Also, change cotton or gauze frequently.

Step 6: Remove the soiled diaper underneath the baby and replace it with a new one.

Some suggest placing the new diaper underneath the baby even before you unfasten and clean the baby. But it does not work for me. You can try it if you want.

Note: place the soiled diaper away from your baby's reach. I've had numerous incidences I don't wish to share. Suffice to say, they were not pretty.

Step 7 Before securing the new diaper, make sure your baby is dry.

Also, this is the time to put on anti-rash cream, ointments or petroleum jelly, or whatever your doctor recommends. Once done, fasten the straps of the new diaper.

Note: Make sure that the diaper is not too tight or too loose. Also, the right size of diaper should always be used. Lastly, the weight recommendation on the diaper's label is just a guide. There are times when you need to experiment on the best size for your baby.

Step 8 Sanitize your hands before picking up your baby.

You must keep your hands and surroundings clean.

Congratulations, you just changed your baby's diaper. Now, get ready to do this 6 to 8 times a day. Don't worry, as your child grows, the need to change diapers becomes less frequent.

PRO TIPS TO DIAPERS

Pick the right diapers

Choosing the right diaper can be daunting, especially because the market is filled with numerous options with varied features. However, knowing your baby's needs will help you pick the right one.

Opt for a super-absorbent diaper, so it can absorb multiple wettings and ensures maximum protection from built-up dampness, and prevents rashes.

Make sure you select the right size diaper for a baby as the wrong size will either be too tight, which may cause marks on the baby's skin, or too loose, which may allow waste to escape.

Select a soft and breathable diaper material that is soothing for the baby's skin and prevents irritation and rashes.

Using ultra-thin or lightweight diapers

These days, Ultra products are also available, where the real innovation is to keep the diaper super lightweight, yet their absorption is more than double of regular diapers. This helps as they are lightweight and breathable and also let your baby stay active and comfortable. Remember, a heavyweight diaper doesn't just cause skin rashes but can also make a baby's movements a little slow because of the weight. So, switch to ultra-products for active comfort throughout.

Disposing diapers correctly

Dirty diapers should be properly cleaned and disposed of in the right manner to maintain a healthy and hygienic surrounding environment. If possible, shake the diaper content into the toilet before disposing of it. Then roll up the diaper as tightly as possible into a ball and reseal the adhesive tapes to hold it in place. You can also wrap the diaper in old newspapers and then dispose of it to avoid any odor or spillage. Ensure you wash your hands after you dispose of them.

Cleaning Boys vs Girls

The crucial difference when cleaning a girl's genitals is that you should clean a baby girl's vulva by wiping front to back. The idea is to wipe excrement away from the vulva, which will help prevent urinary tract infections.

Little boy's penises can simply be wiped clean. Do not try to pull the foreskin back and uncircumcised baby boys. Great care should also be taken when wiping a freshly circumcised penis.

Diaper Rash

Most babies will develop some irritation or rash during their first months due to wet diapers. The best way to treat diaper rash is to change your baby's diaper as soon as it gets wet, coupled with liberal use of diaper cream. Clean them carefully with baby wipes, making sure not to rub or scrub which will make the irritation worse. Exposing the area to air for a few minutes will help, and then apply diaper cream on and around the rash before putting it on the diaper. If the rash doesn't clear up, ask your doctor about it.

Handling The Smell

It is hilarious to watch guys gag at the sight of baby poop. Unfortunately, it's a common reaction and not funny at all when it happens to you.

BE PREPARED: keep a small bottle of Vick's Vapor Rub in the diaper bag and put a little dab on both sides of your nose, and use disposable gloves if it helps. If you have a problem, don't let anyone video you unless you want to become internet famous.

REMEMBER: Not everyone gags at the sight or smell of their baby's poop (or spit up), so please don't assume you're going to.

Use the Time to Bond

Finally, while diapering does feel like a chore, it can be an incredibly important time for bonding and learning. While your little one is captive, you should take time to talk, play and touch. One of the best ways to spend the time is for you to talk to the baby about what they're doing, creating a monologue about the sensations and the parts that are being cleaned.

NIGHTIME -- SKELETON IN THE CUPBOARD.

Sleep comes at a premium for you and your baby. That's why you might find yourself asking this question in the middle of the night: Do I need to change my baby's dirty diaper?

During the day, that's a straightforward question. But at night, it's slightly more complicated. On one hand, your baby may have soiled her diaper while sleeping (it's more than likely to happen at least once per night). And on the other hand, you don't want to wake them unnecessarily to change them. So if your baby is still asleep, should you risk waking them to change the diaper?

Luckily, the answer is simple and will mean you can get the most rest possible. Unless your baby is extremely wet or has pooped, you can probably let them sleep. Believe it or not, there's no need to wake your baby every time they wet their diaper a little. Many of today's diapers are so absorbent that your baby may be able to sleep through the night, or as long as they're capable, even if they've wetted one. When they wake up on their own, or you need to wake them for a feeding, you'll have a chance to clean them up and put on a fresh diaper. Until then, you can probably rest easy (emphasis on rest. New parents need as much as they can get!).

Now I know what you're thinking, "Okay smarty pants, I get that I don't need to change my baby's diaper every single time they wet it in the middle of the night, but what about when I do need to change them at night? What then? And can you tell me in an easily digestible listicle format?" Well, that's an oddly specific request, but don't worry, we've got you covered.

How To Get In And Out Without Disrupting Sleep

Every time you interact with your baby, you naturally want to maximize bonding time. And changing diapers, believe it or not, presents a wonderful bonding opportunity.

Turning your head away in disgust to get it over with as quickly as possible isn't what we mean. We know that you probably use this time to get some eye contact going and to communicate with your baby. You might sing a song, give a tummy raspberry, or just work your magic to make the experience fun.

But that's actually exactly how not to change a diaper in the middle of the night. Here are five things to do:

Establish a Routine

Routines are great when it comes to babies. Babies like routines because it comforts them. And parents like them because routines help set the foundation that there are certain rules to follow. Newer baby monitors like Nanit even track your baby's sleep and let you know when your bedtime routine is becoming inconsistent, as this can result in more sleepless nights for you and your child.

You may think that because your diaper change routine during the day involves eye contact and general playfulness, you should maintain the same routine at night. You can do that, but expect your baby to fully wake up if you do. Setting up a special nighttime diaper change routine will help your baby go back to sleep.

Change diaper at bedtime

Changing your baby's diaper at bedtime will give you both the best chance at a full night's sleep, so consider making that a part of the nightly routine. If your baby has sensitive skin and you're worried they might develop diaper rash from a wet diaper, you can try applying diaper cream before bed. That might help keep them comfortable and asleep, and spare you both a diaper change.

Use dedicated nighttime diapers

You may also want to use the most absorbent diapers at night. During the day, these more expensive varieties might not be worth the extra price. But at night, the extra absorption could mean the difference between deep sleep and a sleepless night.

Make sure baby's diaper fits well

The fit of a diaper is paramount. That's never more important than during the night. Finding a snug diaper could be a matter of trying a handful of sizes and styles until you find one that fits your baby's body and is comfortable but won't leak. Some parents have success with cloth diapers, which can be very absorbent and comfortable.

Be in Stealth Mode

When your baby wakes during the night, the idea is to get them back to sleep as soon as possible. Just as lights and stimulation make it tough for you to fall back asleep, they do the same for your baby. Your goal is to get in and out of the room as quickly and quietly as possible, like a sneaky cat burglar.

Change Poopy Diapers

Remember, if you see (or smell) that your baby pooped their diaper, you need to change it. Whatever you do, don't turn on the overhead light. You want to keep the room dark. Installing dimmers on the lights or using a nightlight are both good options for nighttime diaper changes. Change the diaper as matter-of-factly and gently as possible, and do not look into your baby's eyes. This will only excite them. Your goal is to send the message that this is not playtime. Once you've changed the diaper, put your baby back to bed.

Expert tip: Use a wipe warmer at night. Cold wipes are more likely to wake your baby than warm ones.

Leave Wet Diapers Alone

Again, you can leave a wet diaper alone during the night, waiting until morning to change it — unless your baby's diaper is soaked through to their pajamas. If you're concerned about diaper rash, the Mayo Clinic recommends using some type of barrier ointment, one that contains petroleum jelly or zinc oxide. You can use this diaper ointment each time you change your baby's diaper, or you can use it before bed only. You also might wish to use a high-quality or overnight diaper, which should keep your baby dry and comfortable during the night.

Change Before You Feed

If your newborn baby is awake for a feeding, there are two good times to change their diaper and one not-so-good time. Change your baby before the mom change sides (or halfway through the bottle). This usually wakes babies up enough to get them to take a full feeding. If that wakes your baby too much, change their diaper first, and then feed them. If you change the diaper after you feed your baby, you risk completely waking them again.

PART III

STILL A DAD - SET SOME RULES AND PLAY MORE ROLES

Recently, I moderated a black men's seminar at Zahra's bookstore in Inglewood, California. The group present consisted of about 20 men and 7 women. Silly as it may sound, we figured that there's no bottom line, no official guide, no absolute authority on raising kids, so there are literally hundreds of books on how to be a good parent and raise kids right. One book says if your baby cries, pick them up. Another book says let 'em cry it out. A third book says pick them up once, then let them cry it out. A fourth... well, you get the idea. So how do you know which one is right? you must do the research and decide for yourself. However, believe it or not, your research includes following the guidelines given in this part of the book.

Also, this part is not just about your baby. It is also about you; from maintaining your sanity to balancing yor finances.

12

THE NEW DAD MINDSET

"Fathering is not something perfect men do, but something that perfects the man."

— FRANK PITTMAN

A few years ago, while my wife's baby bump got bigger and my daddy reading list grew longer, I felt cautiously optimistic that this parenthood thing would, somehow, suddenly click one day. The baby would come, instincts would kick in, and the transition from an established couple to a new family would be tiring but not baffling because I was preparing for fatherhood. I thought I knew what to expect the first year.

Bruh was I wrong.

This is not an attempt at what so many fathers seem to revel in: scaring the heck out of fathers-to-be with an eye-rolling mix of martyrdom and schadenfreude. This preparing for fatherhood thing isn't going to rob you of all freedoms, friendships, and fun.

But there are certainly a few things that, in retrospect, I wish I had a heads up about beforehand. Below are six of them:

Above all else: TAKE PATERNITY LEAVE.

First and foremost: if at all possible, take more than just a few days off when your baby arrives. I still have regrets about going back to work too soon after my son's birth. I implore you not to make the same mistake I did. Take as much time as feasible.

If your employer has a paternity leave policy, take the time. If your employer doesn't have a paternity leave policy, make the time. Push the envelope—it's worth it.

You're only a new dad once. Your family needs you more than your boss does right now. Just as importantly, you need them. Invest time in bonding with the baby and establishing a co-parenting dynamic that lays the groundwork for child-rearing equality.

Emails can wait. Embracing your new role as a dad cannot. Take the time, even if it means burning vacation and/or sick days. Put your visions of parenting grandeur on the shelf. Specifically, right next to the diapers, powders, ointments, and breast pump.

When my wife was six months pregnant, I couldn't wait to play catch with my son in the yard. Six months later, I couldn't wait for him to stop crying so I could get some sleep.

My point: this is a marathon, not a sprint. The whimsical Hollywood moments of fatherhood—ball games, bike rides, BBQs—are years away, and real-life doesn't have montages. But don't let your yearning for more seemingly fulfilling- parenting—the teaching moments that guide them through adolescence and into adulthood —divert you from the mission at hand. Newborn nurturing may be less glorious but it is equally necessary, and rewarding in its own right.

Stay in the now while happily anticipating more interactive parenting periods. It turns out my son needed to crawl before he could walk, and walk before he could play catch.

Listen, learn, and leave ego out of it.

All joys of new fatherhood aside, this is the greatest opportunity you've ever had to develop a valuable new skill: childcare. And you get to do it in the service of people you love. Welcome to Baby U. Your instructors include your beloved wife, parents, and in-laws.

The vast majority of early parenting is logistics. Mastering how to arrange a diaper for maximum dryness (fold the front top an inch in before fastening) is far more important than developing bigger-picture parenting perspectives.

Little humans need little things—learn them with humility.

Your reward—other than the satisfaction of dad duties well done—will be comforting, coagulating insight into how this whole baby thing works. You won't be intimidated when someone's watching you swaddle your baby. You won't be befuddled by how a car seat straps in or a stroller unfolds. It's not magic—it just takes willing-ness and practice

Your wife is more importto run the race effectively than you right now.

This isn't some hackneyed "happy wife, happy life" nonsense. Your marriage of equal halves has one partner who, for biological reasons, needs her spouse to be particularly helpful and supportive right now. And by "right now," I mean the first six months of parenthood, at least.

Your wife is sore, probably feeling less-than-attractive, and potentially experiencing some level of postpartum doldrums. And since you can't breastfeed, she's taking the lion's share of the overnight shift. So add exhausted to the list, too.

Your job, then, is basically "everything else."

Coddle. Clean. Cook (or in my case order takeout). Run errands, walk the dog, and stand guard against unwanted visitors. All woke-ness aside, early parenting roles revert to tradition out of necessity; she has to care for the baby right now, and you have to care for her. Do your duty—and the dishes—with honor and gratitude.

That said, don't bend so far that you end up with resentments.

Let's have a frank discussion about self-respect and marital equilibrium, because both may be tested in early parenthood—for both partners. Though new moms deserve loads of leeway, there are limits to how much they should be marginalized. Her needs—and especially the baby's—are paramount right now. But not to the point where you forfeit all respect and relevance.

Flip on the TV and you'll see how disrespected dads are these days. From Modern Family to Family Guy, the "doofus dad" stereotype permeates society. Don't let it infect your household.

You may be third fiddle right now but remember: you're still in the band. And so long as you're trying, you deserve respect; not because you're a man, mind you, but because you're a well-intending soul navigating new parenthood, too.

This is only temporary.

And by "this" I mean "all of this."

Newborns go through phases and stages with head-spinning speed. As soon as you recognize one pattern, it often gets replaced or redirected by another. Sleeping habits, feeding tendencies, what does and doesn't soothe the baby when they cry all evolve remarkably rapidly.

So if you find yourself in a particularly rough phase, relax. It will pass. And if you find yourself recognizing stages only in their twilight—before their inevitable dissipation—don't kick yourself. That happens to everyone —moms and dads alike, and especially with firstborns.

And even if, like me, you're not prone to sentimentality, do stop to soak this in. You'll only be a new dad once: the pride, the pain, the simple joys, and sleeplessness are all part of it, and all beautiful in their nascent reality.

This is all normal, and an unprecedented opportunity for growth. You are fortunate, durable, and altogether fine.

13

DEFEAT THE FUBB IN YOU

"To love oneself is the beginning of a lifelong romance."

— OSCAR WILDE

"I had about all I could stand," a colleague told his friend. "I had a new boss at work that was driving me totally nuts micromanaging everything I did and violating long-established policies in the process. My brain seemed to be bulging from the stress of the day and all I wanted that evening walking in the door was a little rest. I couldn't wait to get home, play with the kids and just unwind.

"But as I walked in the door, it was clear that a tornado had hit in our living room. Not literally, but it seemed like it. Toys were scattered everywhere, and my sweetheart was suffering from a horrible cold and headache. The three kids were tired and hungry, and there was nothing in the house to eat. And I thought that I had been the victim of a bad day so far - it only went downhill from there."

So many fathers find themselves in situations like this where the stress builds and builds until there is a breakdown. Stress meltdowns can take many forms - headaches, explosions of anger, depression and discouragement, sleeplessness, or just living with emotional pain.

Part of the solution to better handling stress is to learn some stress management techniques which would be a godsend for any father. Unfortunately, eliminating stress in our lives is not possible. But it is possible to manage the stresses that we do experience and to mitigate them so that the impact on our lives is minimized.

These ideas will help you reduce the level of stress at home and make home a place where you do want to be anytime.

Set Aside Some Family Downtime.

The pressures of modern life take their toll on a family. While work and chores are important, so are recreation and play. Make time every day for a little "daddy time" with the children. Telling bedtime stories can be a great way to relax and relieve some stress. Family rituals like family prayer, cuddle time in bed with the family, and Saturday morning breakfasts can be important times for both building relationships and reducing stress.

Make Time To Talk.

So often, stress at home is the result of failed communications. So make sure you talk with your partner and your family regularly. Plan a weekly family night so you can deal with problems before they happen. A family therapist said that his best advice for strong marriages was to set aside 30 minutes each night after the kids are in bed for mom and dad to talk together – no television, no smartphones, and no computer – just talk.

Remember good nutrition and regular exercise. Experts on stress management suggest we always make time for healthy eating and physical activity. Proper nutrition will give you good fuel to burn and exercise makes your body more efficient. Eating junk food and sitting in front of the computer all day will tend to make you tired and irritable, and increase your personal and family stress levels.

Make Time For Yourself.

In addition to giving time to your partner and family, make sure that dad's needs are met too. Participate in a favorite hobby that makes you a better man, husband, and father. Getting high or just aimlessly surfing the Internet is not as good as a little golf, hiking, reading, or working in the yard. Find what you like to do – what relaxes you - and then do more of it. And if you can involve the kids or your partner in your favorite downtime activities, all the better.

Work It Out.

Good hard physical labor can help relieve stress. Those endorphins that the body releases when you are physically active are natural mood enhancers. So get out and work in the yard if you have one. Build a project. Mow the lawn or rake the leaves. Or go help a neighbor with a project. Train for a 10K run. Hit the gym and lift a few weights or run on the treadmill. Get active and sweat a bit and you will handle the stress better.

Sharpen The Saw.

Leadership and productivity guru Stephen Covey tells about a man who was cutting wood with a dull saw. We all can recognize that such an activity is not very productive. When a friend asks him why he doesn't stop to sharpen the saw, the woodcutter says, "I am too busy sawing to stop to sharpen the saw." We all experience times like this, but our continuing to work with dull tools – mentally, emotionally, and spiritually – is pretty unproductive. So Covey recommends that we take time daily to sharpen our personal saws in four areas: mental, spiritual, emotional/social, and physical. He promises that spending one hour in these pursuits will be a powerful investment in the other 23 hours of the day.

Learn to say no.

Many of the stress factors in our family come from over-programming our time and lives. A good way to moderate the stresses that come from too much to do is to say no to the unimportant. To do that effectively, you have to define what is important and commit to that, and then say no to everything else. World-renowned Pastor Joel Osteen, who has a church in Texas to which 40,000 parishioners come weekly, has found that he has to say no to weddings and funerals, and any other events on Wednesdays and Sundays. Obviously, Sunday is the day he preaches. Wednesday is his day with God and his family first. He is a great example of practicing what he preaches and putting first things first.

Laugh.

There is no better antidote to stress and anxiety than a little laughter. One family that has learned this lesson has In their home DVDs of many years of The Cosby Show, which is a family favorite. When things get a bit stressful, this family often spends 30 minutes watching Cosby, and life is in greater perspective after they have laughed a bit. Read a little funny article or a book, tell stupid jokes, go to a comedy club with your partner, and take the time to laugh. In so many ways, laughter is the best medicine for stress.

If you need help, get it.

When stress gets overwhelming and over time affects your daily life in negative ways, get to a family counselor and get help. Fathers who don't learn to manage stress well often take it out on the people closest to them, and you just can't afford to find yourself there. Regular outbursts, abusive behavior, or loss of control are signs that you may need emotional help. Check with your employer to see if they offer an employee assistance program (EAP) or with your church to see if they have counseling programs. Consider a father's support group in your area. Find resources to be of help when you can't seem to handle them on your own.

Families are too precious to lose, and not handling stress often leads to fractured relationships, emotional and physical separation, and divorce. Keep your stress at a manageable level and make life at home more pleasant, and you will build important family relationships that last a lifetime.

14

MANAGING FINANCES

"We cannot direct the wind, but we can adjust the sails."

— DOLLY PARTON

Each year when Father's Day rolls around, I'm reminded that I wouldn't trade the experience of raising my three kids for the world. But when I think back to how naïve my wife and I once were about the costs of raising children, I can't help wishing we'd been better prepared.

As a new dad (or dad-to-be), you'd better sit down. According to the U.S. Department of Agriculture's annual Expenditures on Children by Families report, a typical middle-income family can expect to spend over $241,000 to raise a newborn child until age 18 -- and that doesn't even include prenatal care or college costs.

That said, I discovered there are two ways to run the race effectively. One way is to plan your finances, and the second way is to minimize the cost of living. I'd call the first approach "the average American masterplan" and the latter "the genius new dad approach."

Let's see how...

Average American Masterplan

Right now, you're probably more worried about getting enough sleep than funding your retirement. But at some point, you'll need to plot out a financial roadmap to ensure your family's future financial security. As one dad to another, here are a few strategies I've learned that can help

Start saving ASAP

It's hard to save for the future when you present expenses are so daunting, but it's important to start making regular contributions to several savings vehicles, even if only a few dollars at a time.

Establish an emergency fund with enough cash to cover at least six months of living expenses. If that goal seems unattainable, start small: Have $25 or $50 a month from your paycheck or checking account automatically deposited into separate savings account so you never see it, to begin with.

Even if retirement is decades away, the sooner you start saving and compounding your interest, the faster your savings will grow. If your employer offers 401(k) matching contributions, contribute at least enough to take full advantage of the match: A 50 percent match is the same as earning 50 percent interest on savings.

Once those two accounts are well established, open a 529 Qualified State Tuition Plan to start saving for your children's education.

If funding these accounts seems impossible, look for a few luxuries you could cut from your budget for six months -- lattes, going out to lunch, premium cable, etc. After six months have passed, evaluate whether they were actual "needs" or simply "wants" you can live without.

Get insured.

If your family depends on your income, you must be prepared for life's unexpected events, whether an accident, illness, unemployment, or death. Make sure you've got adequate coverage for:

Health insurance. Everyone needs medical insurance, no matter how young or healthy. Just remember: Lower-premium medical plans aren't necessarily cheaper overall; factor in copayment, deductible and prescription costs, in- and out-of-network charges, and exclusions when choosing a policy.

Homeowner/renter's insurance. Don't let theft, fire, faulty plumbing, or other catastrophes leave your family without a home or possessions. To reduce premiums, consider choosing a higher deductible. And opt for "replacement cost" vs. "actual cash value" coverage so your items will be replaced in today's dollars, rather than after depreciation has been factored in -- it's more expensive coverage but worth the extra cost.

Life insurance.

Depending on your family's size and ages, you'll probably want coverage worth at least five to 10 times your annual pay -- more, if you want to cover college costs. And don't forget to insure your spouse's life so you'll be protected as well.

Disability insurance.

Millions of Americans suffer disabilities serious enough to make them miss work for months or years at a time; yet many forego disability insurance, potentially leaving them without an income after a serious accident or illness. Learn details of your employer's sick leave and short-term disability benefits and if a long-term disability is offered, consider buying it.

Car insurance.

Almost every state requires insurance if you own or drive a car -- and for good reason: It protects you financially should you cause an accident or be hit by an uninsured driver. Make sure you have sufficient liability coverage to protect your net worth and income -- it only takes one serious accident to wipe out your savings.

Get Organized

Make sure your affairs are in order in case something should happen to you. Organize files for:

- Medical, homeowner/renter, auto, life, disability, and long-term care insurance policies.
- Banking, credit card, and loan accounts, including passwords for online account management.
- A will (and possibly a trust) outlining how you want your estate managed after death.

A durable power of attorney and health care proxy specifying who will make your financial and medical decisions if you become incapacitated. Also, a living will tells doctors which medical treatments and life-support procedures you do or don't want to be performed. If the primary assignee is your spouse, choose alternates as well, in case you're both impacted.

Birth certificate, marriage license, Social Security card, funeral and burial plans, safe deposit box information, and other important paperwork.

With all these documents, keep in mind:

Review them regularly and make updates when situations change. Make sure that designated beneficiaries for your will, life insurance, and retirement plan accurately reflect your current wishes. For example, if a beneficiary dies or a new child is born, you may want to amend the documents.

Make sure your homeowner's insurance accurately reflects inflationary increases to the value of your home and its contents.

Make backup copies of everything (and photos/videos of possessions) and store them in a few safe locations.

And finally, spend responsibly. If you buy things you don't really need or can't afford, you'll just end up having to work longer hours to pay for them -- time you could have spent watching your kids growing up.

The Genius New Dad

If you had gone through what I went through, you wouldn't mind this approach. You'll have no shame asking for help or better put... helping yourself.

When my wife and I had our first child, no one really told us about financially planning for a baby or about money-saving tips that would be helpful to a new family. We just had to wing it.

I don't want you to wing it. I want you to be prepared as possible for life with a newborn. If you already have a little one… or little ones… at home, I want this to be the motivation you need to get your finances in check

How can you afford a baby?

This is one of those "learn from my mistakes," money-saving tips for new dads. Before we had our first child, I did what any dad is supposed to do: I sold off my man toys – sports car, my collection of random sports memorabilia. But I didn't realize there was more that could be done.

The truth was that before we brought our newborn home, we should have set a budget – the same budget we would have to stick to as new parents – so that we wouldn't have to sort it out in the middle of learning to be parents.

So, make sure you do what we didn't do. Spend a few months living with the new budget before you have to. Trust me, it will save you LOTS of headaches and heartbreaks.

Nurse instead of formula

If it's physically and emotionally possible for your partner to nurse, I highly recommend it. The baby books and blogs might say that it doesn't matter, but from a financial perspective, you will thank me later.

It's estimated that families spend $1700 on formula during the first year of their child's life.

A child costs approximately $250,000. Think about the other important places you could spend that money!

Make your own baby food

Have you ever read the label on a jar of baby food? If you have, you know that this is actually much easier than it sounds. The baby food companies make money because they make it convenient for parents.

- The reality is that you can do it yourself. What are the benefits of making your own baby food?
- You will know exactly what's in the food that you're putting in your child's body.
- You will spend 1/3 the amount of money that you would spend on pre-packaged baby food.
- You will learn the names of all of those vegetables you hated as a kid.
- Get hand-me-down clothes and toys.

I'll be honest. Before I had a child, I swore up and down that I would never let him play with toys that belonged to another kid or wear clothes that had already been worn.

But I was quickly hit in the face with the sheer cost of baby toys and clothes. Along with that, I realized that a newborn grows so fast, it's nearly impossible to keep up with. Because of the savings, I took all the hand-me-downs, from friends and siblings that I could get my hands on.

Buy Used

As I said, I was hesitant to buy used clothes or let my child play with toys that weren't new. If you're similar to me in that regard, I suggest you do the math. Your kids won't care that they are playing with someone else's John Deere tractor and your pocketbook will thank you, too. Here are some great places to utilize for quality used toys and clothes:

- Facebook Marketplace
- Craigslist
- Once Upon a Child
- Local consignment shop
- Kidizen Kid Resale Marketplace
- Go To The Library

Walt Disney once said, "There is more treasure in books than in all the pirate's loot on Treasure Island."

A parent's job is to open his child's mind to the world's treasures that can only be found in books. One glance at Barnes and Noble and you'll see that buying just a few children's books can cost you over $50. When you compare $50 with the library that is... well... free... the choice gets pretty clear. The question is why would you spend all that money on something that you could just get for free?

Eat At Home

In the last two decades, people have become more ambivalent about cooking and eating at home. In fact, one study discovered a family that had unknowingly accrued $30,000 in credit card debt JUST from eating out.

Along with a decrease in cooking at home, people are increasingly eating out for lunch every day. And if a person were to eat out every day for a year, spending $10 each time, they would spend a minimum of $2,500.

Don't fall into the same trap as a large portion of Americans. Just like you could spend 1/3 less on baby food if you make your own, you would spend 1/3 less on food if you eat at home. And, on the plus side, your savings will outweigh the annoyance of having to do dishes!

Buy In Bulk

Finally, if you have the resources and access to Costco, you can cut the cost of having children by saving at least 20% on your purchases. How? Buying in bulk. In addition to financial savings, there are other benefits:

- Less packaging means you don't have to manage as much waste.
- Collecting a lot of the essentials means you are prepared for an emergency. There's no need for extra stress in the face of an emergency when there's a newborn at home.
- Buying in bulk means fewer trips to the store. Enough said.

Children are expensive blessings. They bring joy to our lives while, at the same time, costing us around $250,000. If you do the math, it's easy to get over-whelmed and think, "How will I afford a baby?"

I've been there before and I know that just thinking about bringing home a newborn can bring stress into your life. But, trust me. If you can put some of these money-saving tips for new dads into practice, you can take hold of what might feel like something out of your control.

15

COACHING YOUR CHILD

"It is easier to build strong children than to repair broken men"

— FREDERICK DOUGLAS

Have you ever wondered how independent your child actually is or would be? Will your child be able to look after themselves if left alone for a while? Do you think your child is well-equipped with essential life skills to face the world?

Remember those times you would ask about spending the night at a friends' house or about going over to someone's house to play? How many times did your parents say, "No. They are a bad influence on you?" If they never said it, they were thinking it!

Think about it!

It's absolutely important for children to learn more than just academically. And no, enrolling them in various activity classes isn't enough either. Your children would be happier to learn some of these skills from you.

Before we get started, please be reminded that there are no one-fits-all skills to teach children as this will vary due to various factors, such as gender, age, location, etc. You should carefully read and decide the best skills you think your child needs to know.

So, let's look at a few skills that are essential for any growing child to learn in order for them to find it easy to deal with adulthood and how you can teach your child these skills.

BASIC SELF-DEFENCE:

I'm sure you'll agree that in today's world especially, safety is of utmost importance, and developing self-defence not only makes the child feel more independent, but also more confident.

Basic self-defence is a must — be it for your son or your daughter. Most schools these days invest in teaching basic self-defence to children. But if your child's school does not, don't hesitate to send them for classes outside.

FIRST-AID AND THE IMPORTANCE OF HEALTH:

You can't expect to always be around whenever your child gets hurt, a bite or a rash! So how about empowering them such that they are able to take care in case of an emergency until they reach a grown-up?

This is essentially something the child's schooling should cover but I strongly encourage its reinforcement at home by teaching your child essential first aid steps.

And this you can do by showing them a first aid kit and its contents. Children are, after all, excellent learners!

Another important skill is teaching your child to take care of their health. Instead of forcing your child to eat vegetables, talk to them about health risks in eating junk food all the time and explain how the healthy food will benefit them in a way that they can apply to themselves.

For example, for a kid interested in sports, talk about foods that give them increased stamina and agility, enabling them to play better at their sport.

For kids that care about physical appearance traits like hair, talk about the importance of Omega-3 fatty acids and the foods that contain it.

MAKE THEM DO THEIR OWN WORK:

Let's face it. When our kids grow up, they are very likely to leave home to pursue their education or career. And if they aren't taught responsibility and daily-living skills today, it would be a problem for them in the future.

Most parents run around doing everything for their children so much so that the child doesn't get involved in anything. This shouldn't be the case.

Be it putting their school bag together or taking the plate to the kitchen, ensure your child is 'responsible' for their work. Teach these skills now, before it's too late! And there will be another helping hand at home, isn't it?

PRO TIP: You can also try an activity box like Flintobox to make a child learn and develop skills independently.

The activities in Flintobox are highly educational where children learn concepts and life skills through play!

HOW TO MANAGE TIME:

You're probably wondering how. Well, you can do this by getting your kid to claim responsibility for their own time.

Do this by getting them an alarm clock that they can use to wake up on time for school, instead of you waking them up.

Get them a planner to use to track their school work and other extra-curricular work and to keep track of what needs to be done by when.

When they do this, they will automatically begin to allow specific amounts of time for play and for work.

DECISION-MAKING SKILLS:

Education, career, life partners — there are so many important decisions we need to make in our lives. How about instilling the skill of making appropriate decisions at an early age itself in your child?

Here's how to — teach them in small and simple ways how to make wise decisions. Start by asking them to choose between 2 activities or games; 2 different types of clothes; 2 different food items, etc.

Once this happens, the child will understand the consequences that each decision causes. So guide your child through the process, help them weigh the advantages and disadvantages before they make their decision!

MANAGING MONEY & BASIC BUDGETING:

This is quite a basic one among life skills. Give your children a certain amount of pocket money every week or every two weeks that they have to use for their expenses.

If they wish to buy something a little more expensive, ask them to save up their pocket money to buy it.

Or, you can lend them a helping hand by telling them that for every chunk of money they save, you'll add a certain amount of money to their fund for buying the product.

This will motivate them more. I think the concept of comparative shopping also comes under the concept of teaching your child about budgeting.

Tell them why you choose comparatively cheaper options sometimes. When they want to buy a few things when you go shopping, encourage them to pick one or two items if they're of the same kind.

This kind of budgeting training develops a habit in your child to not waste money and to respect its value.

I believe understanding the importance of money and managing it is something that every child above the age of 10 should know.

They are introduced to the concept of money from the age of 7 in school via subjects like Maths but nobody teaches them the importance and relevance of budgeting, planning, saving and the real value of money as they have never handled money in real life.

Open a bank account for your child, ask them to deposit some money every month (money received as gifts or if they help out in the house with some tasks you could pay them a small amount.) This will inculcate the habit of saving and appreciating money.

SHOPPING SKILLS:

Always take your child grocery shopping with you. Once your child knows where the different categories of items are shelved, give them a basket and ask them to get a few easy-to-find things for you.

You can also keep your kid in charge of buying a few things every month. Examples of this would be snacks and juices. Once done, teach them how to pay for it!

And the most important point — don't forget to model smart shopping yourself!

INVOLVE THEM IN SIMPLE COOKING:

Children can cook, too! Don't you agree?

And you can start with simple things! Teach your child how to make their own peanut butter and jam sandwiches, teach them how to butter a slice of bread, and how to make a salad.

Have them tear up greens, squeeze lemons, and put chopped vegetables together to make a salad.

You can also get them to help you with baking, with handing you ingredients while you cook or with keeping the kitchen table clean while you're preparing a meal.

IMPORTANCE OF ENVIRONMENTAL PRESERVATION:

Instilling the importance of environment and sustainability at an early age will teach your child to be more loving towards the planet. Teach your kid why preserving the environment is essential by making small lifestyle changes at home. Get them to practise eco-friendly habits in everything they do.

You can also make them do environmental activities such as gardening and collecting waste to throw in a bin. If you have a yard, give them a portion of the yard to plant whatever they like in.

Help them sow seeds and make it their responsibility to water the plants. If you don't have a yard, you can always use planting pots.

FINISH TASKS INDEPENDENTLY:

Let your children do their own tasks. Let them pack their own school bag, make their own bed, and even pack their own lunch!

You can do this by making each task a bit exciting by helping them out. Buy them new bedding and cushions themed around a cartoon or movie they love.

Have a sandwich station or a pancake station for breakfast with cut-up fruits, jams, syrup, spreads, etc, so they can make their own plate and eat it the way they like.

HOW TO INTERACT WITH PEOPLE:

We've all taught children about stranger danger but this doesn't make much logical sense considering every person we're close to as adults was a stranger to us at some point.

Instead, teach your children to do exactly what adults do. Teach them to differentiate between good strangers and bad strangers. Teach them how to interact with good strangers.

Teach them how to make friends, how to be friendly to good adults, and just how they should go about interacting with these people.

If you think about it, a task that we do every single day is to be engaged in interaction with people. If we don't teach children this at a young age, they may not develop positive social skills.

CLEANING AND OTHER HOUSEHOLD CHORES:

Now I know what you're thinking. Getting kids to get involved in cleaning activities is really hard! We agree. But we assure you that your effort will be well worth it!

Start small by just asking them to keep their room clean, make their bed, and make sure everything they own is in its right place. You can then ask them to clean the dishes that they use to eat after eating as well.

You can ask them to dust the tables one day and ask them to take the trash out on another; you can also ask them to set the table in whichever way they think looks the best and ask them to get creative with it.

Ask them to participate in chores such as these to help you out or in exchange for their allowance.

It's important to practise these activities both in the context of an allowance and out of it, so your child learns to just help out without being given anything in return, too.

BASIC ETIQUETTES & HOW TO ORDER AT RESTAURANTS:

Teach your kid about how to behave at a restaurant and how to place an order. Ask them to place their own orders and decide on what they want to eat on their own.

Also, teach them how to eat with a knife and fork, how to place the knife and fork on the plate once they're done eating, and on how to tip the waiters.

HOW TO USE MAPS:

Going somewhere? Start off by teaching your kids the routes around your house and test this by asking them to direct you home or to school the next time you're dropping them.

You can then ensure that your child learns how to read a map, and also teach them how to use a GPS and follow its instructions.

BASICS OF TRAVELLING:

Aside from navigation, your child should know travelling basics.

From learning to ride a cycle to learning how to use public transport, make sure your child knows how to do these things along with routes.

Teach them how to buy metro or bus tickets, teach them the basics of which metro train or bus goes to your house from school. These are important skills that your child will need for later as well as for emergencies.

LOOKING AT SITUATIONS FROM OTHERS' PERSPECTIVES:

When your child comes to you about a problem that he or she had with their friend or a problem that they witnessed, encourage them to look at the situation that took place from the perspective of others.

Even explain the emotional reactions of people every chance you get. Explain why someone is sad or angry.

This increases their problem-solving abilities and their level of understanding of the people around them greatly.

RESILIENCE & ADAPTABILITY:

Another important skill would be to teach your child to be resilient. How you can do this is by ensuring you don't feed your child with solutions all the time.

Empower your child to problem-solve by themselves so that they're ready to face challenges as and when they come. They must learn resilience to adapt to different changes and different environments.

Make sure you have an open channel of communication to understand what your child is going through and help them out – and of course, as a parent, you too must model resilient behaviour at home!

CONCLUSION

There are experiences we go through in life, that change us forever. Fatherhood, for me, was one of them. It changed my perspectives on many things, including the role that women play in the furtherance of life.

Therefore, if you got nothing else out of this book than the fact that you need to play a larger role in your partner's pregnancy, then I will call this book a success. Be there, be present. Go to the appointments and the classes and take an active part in what is going on. Times have changed. No longer is it acceptable for fathers to just sit back and allow their wives to take care of the children. Show her that you understand that.

I know that we've talked a lot about how you can help her, but it's important to remember that this is your baby too. Do not for one second think that you have it as hard as she does at any point in the process of raising a baby, but do remember that you are important and you still play a vital role in your baby's upbringing. Too often, I see men taking the backseat to their partners when it comes to babies. And yes, while she does have a very strong opinion about how she wants things to do be done, that doesn't mean that you can't give your two cents too. If you want something that your lady doesn't or vice versa, speak up. The baby is just as much yours as it is hers.

Be a part of the process, not just a spectator. Be there. She will appreciate it, eventually. She will love and appreciate you all the more for making the effort. Though, the fact that you're using this book and searching for ways to help on the internet is already a good sign.

And, lastly, remember that you're important too. Take care of yourself, seek help, take breaks, and remember that fatherhood is not something perfect men do. Rather, it is something that perfects the man. If all you did today was to wake up and try again, I'm proud of you!

FIRST TIME FATHER' BABY'S FIRST YEAR

THE ULTIMATE FIRST TIME DADS' GUIDE FROM BABY TO TODDLER

BOOK DESCRIPTION

This heartfelt, funny, and insightful book about fatherhood is about a father preparing himself for his newborn baby. This book delves into the nitty-gritty of what it is to be a father whilst understanding and going through all the changes and challenges. Penned in a conversational manner, this book will take you on the author's journey of learning about parenting through his experiences. It has great advice for new dads, how to be the best dad to your child, a supportive partner, and look after your own needs as well, all written down with a sprinkling of real-life stories and anecdotes to keep you entertained.

Practical guide for new dads, from your baby's birth to their first birthday

Newborns don't come with a manual, but *We're Parents!* is the next best thing. Adrian Kulp (a four-time dad himself) offers fast, fun, and easy-to-digest advice that makes it simple for you to step up and do your part as a brand-new dad.

Wondering how to burp your newborn? Not sure how to get them to try solids? Desperate to get them to sleep? This comprehensive guide breaks your baby's first year down into quarterly chunks, offering stage-specific advice, quick reference guides, tutorials, monthly stats and goals, and a healthy dose of humor to help you be a supportive partner and great dad to your little one.

This standout among new dad books includes:

• **Step-by-step how-tos**—Find detailed guidance for common situations you'll encounter as a new dad, from soothing and swaddling your newborn to spotting food allergies and baby-proofing your home.

• **Cheat sheet checklists**—Get quarterly checklists of ways you can help around the house, with mom and the baby, and with events and medical appointments.

• **Developmental milestones**—Track your baby's development at a glance with charts that lay out the most important milestones in one place.

Discover how to be the best father and husband you can be with the expert advice inside *We're Parents!*

INTRODUCTION

Parenting through the perspective of a father/ What does a father think about parenting?/ I'm a dad, now what?/Does every dad feel the same way?/

A couple of my best friends and I were at a downtown sports bar on a Saturday night watching the A Lakers and Chicago Bulls basketball game. It was a close game, so all of us were on the edge of our seats, rooting for the Lakers because we lived in Los Angeles (LA). While sipping on our chilled beer, watching the game in anticipation, one of my friends kept receiving repeated calls. We told him to either accept the call or put his phone on silent mode. He disappeared in between the game, and by the time he returned, the Lakers had won, and the entire bar had erupted into celebrations.

"That was my wife. I have to rush because my son is not feeling well, sorry guys." That is all he said, and he sped out of the bar without us getting the chance to get a word in. While I felt concerned for him, I was also grateful for not having child and family issues in my life. I was 28-years old, single, had a great paying job in an accounting firm, and marriage and children were nowhere on the horizon for me. My other friend and I joked about how glad we were to not be in his situation, cheered for being single, drank late into the night, only to wake up with a terrible hangover the following day.

I distinctly remember the next morning. I dragged myself out of bed, made myself a cup of warm brewed coffee, called the following day asked about his son (who was fine by then, it was about teething issues), and told him how he missed out on a great night. His answer, which made no sense at all, was, "Buddy, I'm sure you two had a great time, but I had to be there for my family, and honestly, that was good enough for me." I could not relate to him, and while I said yes I understood him, I secretly thanked God for not putting me in such a situation.

Fast forward five years, and I can now completely relate to that conversation. Life is funny. I am a father to a three-year-old daughter, and I cannot imagine my life without her many instead discouraged of a life where I am not a father. Fatherhood is beautiful and comes with a bag of mixed emotions. I remember when my wife, Anna, told me she was pregnant; I was ecstatic and began to tear up. I wanted to be the best father to our child, and I decided to prepare myself as much as I could before the delivery of our child. However, when I set out to buy books and attend classes on parenting, I was pretty disappointed that there was not much material available for fathers-to-be. When I asked other friends who were fathers how they prepared for their child, the usual response was 'we winged it, bro,' or 'take it as it comes.' Honestly, that was not helpful at all; instead, discouraged, it was surprising. I felt so slightly lost and discouraged and decided to read up on a lot of pregnancy books for mothers, which helped me be a better and understanding husband to my wife, though it did not help me much in what was in store for me as a new father. Maybe historical and patriarchal stereotypes were at play here; however, I did as much research I could and began my journey of fatherhood. Hence, here I am today with all my experience to help new fathers cope and navigate with the new experience of becoming a parent. It is a rollercoaster of emotions, filled with joy, love, happiness, being overwhelmed, overworked, under-slept, smiles and laughter. Fatherhood changes one's life entirely, and you start feeling differently towards various relationships and aspects in your life. Billions of people have become parents; however, until you do not become one yourself till you do not become one yourself, you cannot comprehend how incredible the experience is.

It is a given that a child shares a beautiful bond with the mother, since the child emerges from the mother's womb, it is a symbiotic relationship. However, I feel the connection and bond between the father and the new-born baby are usually overlooked or ignored, which is unfortunate because the father is a parent as well and needs to be involved in the child's life as much as possible.

Throughout the book, I will chronicle the beginning of fatherhood, along with how I prepared, how I helped my wife, the challenges I faced while balancing work and home life, dealing with my child's health, and learning to take care of myself. Becoming a parent is a massive responsibility – emotional, physical, and financial, hence think of starting a family when you think you are ready and not 'just because it is the natural next step.' Once you do become a father, remember to be patient with yourself because you are doing the best you can with whatever resources you have available to you.

1

WELCOMING OUR CHILD INTO
THIS WORLD

Anna and I met at a common friend's dinner, and we hit it off immediately. We began dating a week after we met and got married a year later. She is a wonderful and supportive partner and an amazing mother. I would also like to add that I am an amazing father. Anna and I had returned from her 5-year-old nephew's Spiderman-themed birthday party and were talking about how adorable the children were. We were sitting on an island in the kitchen, sipping on wine, and she asked me how I felt about starting a family. Of course, we had discussed having a child a few times, but we had never really thought about it in detail. But at that moment, it felt as if I was ready to become a father and start a family with Anna. In retrospect, it could have been the wine and images of cute children at play.

This conversation was two years into our marriage. We had a conversation about it the next morning as well and spoke in length about our savings and how we will manage our work-life along with our baby. If Anna and I were to have this discussion three years ago, I would have said no to trying for a baby, but it felt right in the moment because I knew I was as ready as I could be. I knew I was ready to take on the responsibility willingly and give out care and love. You can never be 100% ready, but you will know when you are as ready as you can be. And hence began my journey into perspective fatherhood.

There are numerous couples who have unplanned pregnancies as well. If you are one of them and find yourself in a situation that you had not planned for, it is understandable to be overwhelmed or anxious. However, it is best to take it one day at a time, come to terms with reality, which is you will be a father within the year, and have a conversation with your partner about the following issues;

- Accepting the current reality and the situation
- Establish a financial plan
- Planning and being proactive,
- Reading and researching about everything pregnancy-related
- Preparing for the baby – paternity leave, baby-

THE FIRST TIME FATHER 2-IN 1 VALUE BUNDLE | 261

proofing the house, designing a space for the baby, packing hospital bags, and figuring out a pregnancy plan.

You and your partner are in the same boat; hence both of you need to support each other during this time and make the best of what you have; hurry. If you need support from your friends and family, make sure to reach out to them.

Eleven months into our conversation, Anna was pregnant with our baby girl. She had a rounded belly and was ready to give birth at any given time. It was a Monday, and I was at the office when I received a call from Anna, "My water has broken; hurry home, please." She had gone into active labour. I left work as soon as possible, rushed home, grabbed our hospital bags that we had prepared for the hospital in advance, and drove to the hospital.

In Anna's bag we had packed;

- Nursing bras
- Comfortable pajamas
- Medicines
- Toiletries
- A dressing gown
- Comfortable slippers

- Maternity underwear
- A pack of muslins (to clean up the new-born's bodily fluids)
- Towels
- Maternity pads
- Phone charger
- Going home outfit

For the baby we packed;

- Baby clothes (sleepsuits and a pack of vests)
- Blanket
- Socks
- Nappies
- Baby wipes
- Car seat

I packed for myself;

- Clothes
- Phone charger
- Toiletries
- Hospital paperwork, ID, and insurance card
- Snacks

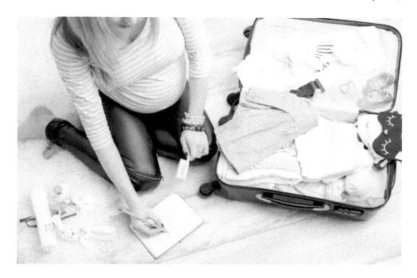

It is convenient and time-efficient to have these bags ready in advance a week before your wife's delivery time. This way, you will be prepared whenever your wife goes into labor. All you have to do is load the bags into the car and head to the hospital.

She is coming!

I remember Anna being relatively calm on our way to the hospital. I had called our gynaecologist when Anna told me that she was going into labour for them to be prepared when we got there. She was admitted to the room; her vitals were checked and monitored, and then the process began when the doctor told us that Anna was 9 cm dilated. We had prepared a birth plan as well. It is another important tip I would like for everyone to follow. It makes the process of childbirth smoother and irons out any creases or bumps. Anna and I included the following in our birth plan;

- Which hospital or birthing centre she would give birth at
- The environment she would like
- Who she wanted in the room?
- If she wanted any pain controlling medications
- Who will cut the umbilical cord?

These are common questions and it is great to have answers to them beforehand rather than scurrying around at the last minute and adding more than what is require on your plate. While following a birthing plan is wonderful, remember to stay flexible in case of an emergency.

We had decided I would be with Anna in the delivery room. Anna's family and my family were extremely understanding about our decision. Usually, hospitals have policies about how many people are allowed into a delivery room, hence it is advisable to check beforehand with the hospital and let your family know accordingly. Moreover, ask your partner what she prefers and what she is comfortable with.

The process was long and tiring for Anna, as it was for me. But being there for her, cheering her on, and staying strong really helped her through the entire process. Honestly, it is not an easy process, and hats off to women for going through this. When our baby girl, Ella, came into this world Anna and I both cried because we were so overwhelmed with joy and exhaustion at the same time. It was a beautiful yet tiring experience. Anna was drained but when she saw Ella it was as if she had been reenergized, I knew we would have different experiences of first holding her, I also felt slightly insecure and thought will I be able to be as important as Anna in Ella's life and I checked myself and reminded myself that our process and our love will be different, yet present from both ends. Anna held Ella first and I took a few pictures of their first moments together, and then the nurse handed Ella over to me. I do not think I have been left speechless before, but when I first held my daughter, I was left speechless. She was bundled up in a light pink blanket, her cherubic face matching the colour of her blanket. Her eyes were semi-shut, and I like to believe she was smiling at me, but that could also be my delusional happiness speaking. It was like magic, and it was as if I had known her all my life. I held her ever so softly as if she was a fragile doll. I had anticipated this moment for a while, I had read up and researched as much as I could, but when the experience was felt in reality, no amount of reading or hearsay could cover how I felt in the moment. I was overwhelmed by a feeling of love and the need to keep her safe. 'She is here and safe with me, Anna. I am a father now,' I remember telling Anna. The moment was incredible for both of us.

Fathers play a vital role during labour and delivery; hence it is essential for you to as a father and a partner to give it your best. With practice and education, you can become an excellent partner, so do not be harsh on yourself. Following are a few tips you can follow once your partner goes into labour. All individuals are unique, so all the tips may or may not apply to you, but you will know what your partner wants to be attuned to her needs and be her anchor.

1. Be a role model to your partner in labour. To put it mildly, it is difficult going through labour. Hence strange things begin to happen to a woman's body. During this moment, observe your partner's breathing pattern. Notice if she is breathing in a shallow manner or if her breathing is fast-paced. Instead of telling your partner, act out an effective method of breathing for her pain management which will help her cope with the pain and stay relaxed. An effective breathing method is taking a deep breath in and a deep breath out repeatedly. Hence, model it visually for her since it will be much easier for her to do the correct breathing when she sees you doing the same. The same goes for body language. If you see your partner hunched up or sitting tense up, instead of saying 'straighten up' or 'sit straight,' you can emulate her posture and shake it out, and she will visually be able to see the effect. In essence, think of yourself as a, and remember that non-verbal communication is assertive. During labour, too much conversation can annoy your partner; it is a physically and mentally demanding situation, after all; hence it is easier to be led with ideas rather than thinking about what she should be doing herself. Plus, it is a thoughtful way of being there for your partner and giving them support when they need it the most.

There are different methods of breathing you can practice during labour. Focused breathing is one. When this technique is practiced it helps to interrupt the transference of pain signals to the brain and also stimulates the release of endorphins which work as pain relief hormones in the body. Another technique of breathing is abdominal breathing, which is often referred to as diaphragmatic breathing as well. This technique works in tandem with the abdominal muscles. While inhaling the abdomen moves outwards and when exhaling the abdomen moves inwards. If you do yoga or practice meditation, you will be familiar with abdominal breathing. The benefit of this technique of breathwork is that it changes brain waves by decreasing stress hormones, reducing blood pressure, and increasing oxygen levels. Work on the breathing technique that works positively for your partner. In order to become familiar with these breathing exercises, you can practice them beforehand, alone or with your partner, because practice makes perfect!

2. Be her number one cheerleader. It is extremely valuable to the process of labour and delivery. It can be hard to remember positive things to say in the labour room and it is easier to say negative things such as 'you look tired' or 'this is taking a long.' Positive reaffirmation is important because it will make your partner feel better. The hack is that you should think of yourself as an actual cheerleader as if you are on the side-lines of a marathon and your partner is running by. Imagine yourself in that situation, I am sure you will definitely not say 'you are tired' or 'is this hard?' while she was running by. Instead, try working with positive affirmations such as 'what you've created is,' 'you're nearly there,' and 'the finish line is coming up.' If your partner has been administered pain medication and doesn't look as active prior to the epidural, believe me, she is. Even during a caesarean, she looks passive; she may not be, so bring your A-game to the labour room.

3. Be the DJ. Music is powerful in labour, it can change the tone, mood, give you energy and keep you calm. Moreover, it can be fun too. Suggesting to make a playlist together, the playlists can be calming, relaxing, active, or even favourites. You can make a playlist of songs that make your partner happy. Get some good equipment, such as a Bluetooth speaker, or play it on your phone. Music acts as a coping mechanism for relaxation. When you get to the hospital and get situated, go ahead and get the playlist on. Sometimes we forget in the entire chaos but do remember to do this. Scientifically, music has the ability to deepen and slow down breathing (which is helpful as mentioned previously), reduces stress, and enables adequate physiological functioning.

4. Hydration. Be the water boy all throughout the labour period because hydration is key for contractions and labour. Dehydration can lead to strange labour patterns or can stop labour altogether. Plus keeping hydrated is extremely doable. However, I suggest that you do it strategically – have a bottle with a straw because it is easier to manage in whatever position your partner may be in. You can even vary the type of liquids, such as electrolytes water, Gatorade, and coconut water. Instead of asking your partner if she is thirsty or if she wants a sip, just take a bottle with a straw and put it next to her mouth. Imagine yourself as a trainer in the NBA, standing on the side-lines. You see trainers come out with squirt bottles, and they just hold it up so they can squirt water into the player's mouth. That is your goal as well. You will want to see her taking a couple of sips between every few contraptions. Remember to hydrate yourself as well, please, because you are the caregiver. You can only do your best if you take care of yourself as well. Staying hydrated can become more vital if the mother opts for an epidural. Hence staying hydrated and loading up on fluids before getting the anaesthesia will decrease the chance of low blood pressure and will also help in recovery post-delivery.

5. Have, give and eat snacks because snacking is vital. Make a snacks shopping list beforehand. You should be eating during labour, and so should your partner. I do not mean a three-course meal, rather intermittent and healthy snacking. It helps labour progress and fuels you along the entire process. The hospital you and your partner choose to give birth at may have a policy that restricts eating during a certain point in labour, or with epidural, or at a certain time of labour so please do check in with your hospital before. Do not ask your partner if is hungry, instead unwrap something and hand it to her. Giving something to eat rather is much more effective than thinking about what to eat. Make sure you are having snacks as well. The snack and water tip are equally important when you get the baby home as well because hydration and eating while breastfeeding is good for the mother. If she sits down to feed the baby, you put a bottle with a straw and some snacks for her as well.

6. Comforting touch. It is important to re-center your partner during the process. You can do a light massaging touch and massage the head slightly; this will assure her you are there by her side and she is safe. A gentle and comforting touch floods our nerve gates with pleasure sensations; hence the mother will not be focusing on uncomfortable sensations. You can also apply counter pressure at this time if that works better for your partner. This practice will help ease your partner's mind and bring her back to a relatively calmer space. She may not like you doing it, but ask her to communicate that to you so you know what to do instead. Remember not to take anything personally. If your partner is in transition, touching or rubbing may become slightly annoying, so be wary and know what your partner wants at the moment.

7. **Ignorance is bliss.** During pushing and birth do not let the mother know she has pooped (it is a completely natural process during pregnancy and it also signals the finish line). Instead, sprinkle some peppermint essential oil onto the mat under your partner. Be by her side, hold her hand, and keep peeking to see the baby's head. Help her to tune into her body and listen to when it is time to push and how long to push for. Nobody knows her body better than herself hence help her tune into her body. If she is on an epidural, she may need help regarding when to and how long to push for. Maybe you can choose to be silent while the nurse or doctor does that. Either you are coaching your partner during the final push or the medical team does that.

Labour is a demanding situation, more so for the mother, hence you and your partner may be at your wit's end. However, try to do your best for your partner and know that you are doing the best you can!

Bringing our angel home

Luckily, Anna had a smooth delivery without any hiccups and Ella was in fine health, hence the doctors gave us the go-ahead to head home after a night in the hospital. Your hospital will arrange all the items you will require for your child once you get discharged and head home with your baby. Make sure you grab any extra diapers, a bulb syringe, an infant hairbrush, and wipes on your way out. Extra items go a long way. Moreover, your hospital may also provide you with numerous lotions, soaps, formula samples, and creams for your baby and the mother. Another checklist to have prepared before getting discharged from the hospital is your baby's health screening checklist. Getting professional medical advice from doctors comes in handy, thus take your time and ask the medical team if you or your partner have any concerns. Moreover, the nursing team at the hospital will check the temperature, jaundice levels, and oversee any vaccines, and schedule a hearing screening.

We headed home happily, going from a family of two to three overnight. Anna, Ella, and I; a picture-perfect family. It is essential to have a car seat prepared for the baby and know how to strap in your new-born with all the harnesses and latches. Anna and I had pre-planned this so we had the house baby-proof and ready for Ella. For Ella, we had chosen a lilac theme for her nursery. Set against a floral wallpaper lay Ella's white DaVinci Kalani crib. For Anna, I had purchased a comfortable cream-colored armchair with a footstool. I had no clue how much time Anna and I would be spending on that chair, it becomes our second bed.

The novelty of our situation had us slightly overwhelmed, I believe I was more anxious and nervous than Anna, and I tried not to be overt about it. Even though my mind was an encyclopaedia on everything baby-related, living in the moment I was pretty uncertain what to do next. A quote by John Green really resonated with me in this situation, "The nature of impending fatherhood is that you are doing something that you're unqualified to do, and then you become qualified while doing it." Anna sensed that and told me to take a deep breath and said the following simple words to me 'let's go with the flow, we've got this.' At that moment, those were the most reassuring words. If you find yourself in a situation similar to mine, repeat that phrase to yourself, because honestly you have got this, and just go with the flow.

Now that we have covered the incredible moments of feeling fatherhood and an immense amount of unconditional love, let's get down to reality. You will most probably be dealing with the following issues once you and your partner return home;

Baby's sleep pattern – Are they sleeping enough?

The aim is to make sure your baby sleeps throughout the night, it sets a pattern and allows the baby to develop the habit of sleeping through the night. However, do not be surprised if your baby sleeps a lot during the day in the first few days, though this cycle will get regulated eventually. Meanwhile, the mother's and the father's sleep patterns will be in sync with the baby's sleep pattern, hence it is an adjustment period for the entire family. The good news is that everyone does adjust. Moreover, make the most of the period when your baby is awake and establish a bedtime routine irrespective of how young your child may be. It is a great pattern to develop early on. When you do put your child to bed, please place them on their back, it is the best position for a new-born baby.

Did the baby just hiccup or let out a gasp? (Discerning between the two can be difficult initially)

Changing the baby's clothes – How do I do it without hurting the baby? Nervous while handling your baby?

We've all been there, after all, new-born babies are so fragile. Therefore, make sure you handle them with gentle and soft care and in order to develop their head and neck muscles, you should use your hand as a support. In order to change the baby's clothes as gently as possible, support their head while manoeuvring their clothes around their small body. Rather than slipping the shirt or pants as is, gather the sleeves or the seams, it is easier to dress your baby that way. Moreover, keep in mind that you must hold your baby upright and support their neck and head when zipping or buttoning them into clothes.

Feeding times and how to decipher what the baby wants

If your partner pumps her breast milk and you are on night feeding duty, make sure late-night feeding is just that, do not try to play with the baby at this time since it might disrupt their pattern. Remember to burp the baby after every two ounces. To all the fathers out there reading this, a mother breastfeeds her new-born for the first few weeks, however, she may choose to pump her breast milk once the nursing period is established. This is where you step in and can divide the feeding time between yourself and your partner. Not only does it relieve your partner and gives her time to tend to her personal time, but it also helps to create a bond between you and your child – what more could you want? Moreover, a new-born will usually cry out for milk, to be held, to be fed, or for a diaper change. Hence, if the baby is crying or squirming know that it is your cue to check the aforementioned needs.

Not so angelic anymore

While it was absolutely wonderful spending time with Ella and dividing tasks with Anna, everyone was running high on emotions and low on sleep. Anna and I had spoken in detail and in-depth about our particular roles and duties, which proved to be helpful, however sometimes those duties may be overlooked in all the chaos of settling down and establishing a routine, which is okay. I believe the manta 'it is okay, I/we can do this really helped Anna and I initially during the postpartum period. Furthermore, Anna and I would make sure we would alternate our nap, eating, and showering times in order for each of us to function in a healthy manner. I had spoken to numerous friends and family members who told me alarming stories of how they did not shower for three days because they did not find the time or how they forgot to eat for the entire day and ending up fighting with their partner over the smallest of issues – being hangry is real. For the first 96 hours, it was all about diaper changes, breastfeeding, sleeping, and tending to Ella crying out. I felt I was living in a time loop. I would find myself nodding off while holding Ella in my arms. It had been two weeks since we had returned from the hospital with Ella, she had been fed and was sleeping. Anna and I decided to open a bottle of wine and just have a conversation. I remember taking a few sips, Anna was talking about

278 | ALFIE THOMAS

something she had read in a magazine, and the next thing I knew was that I fell asleep mid-conversation. Anna loves relating this story to everyone. You can imagine the extent of exhaustion. Fortunately, my company had given me two months of paternity leave which really worked out wonderfully for the entire family. I could bond with Ella, support Anna and help around the house as well. I was able to focus entirely on what I wanted to do. Of course, children are the most wonderful additional component to a family but the reality is that it is hard work and effort, especially during the first week when the baby comes home from the hospital, it requires all your dedication – physical, emotional, and financial.

Moreover, you do not just have your partner and baby to tend to, family and friends also want to visit, and honestly, that is the last thing we wanted to do; socialize. It is okay to draw a boundary and tell your friends and relatives that you will be ready to meet when you actually are settled in and ready to meet. However, if your friends and family desperately want to see you and your baby, then can come to have a peek and could maybe help you out with some chores, such as getting a cooked meal or buy your weekly groceries. I found my best friends to be extremely cooperative and under- standing, they would drop in and say hello and drop off a cooked meal. It made our lives so much easier. A couple of times they came with bottles of wine and dessert, which really helped Anna and I unwind after a long day. Anna and I had decided that we would hire help for the first month to help with household chores and it turned out to be one of the best decisions we made. I do not know how we would have managed to make the beds or do the laundry with Ella around. What's more, our house help was so helpful, we decided to hire her on a long-term basis. Melissa is still with us and is wonderful with Ella. Caring for a baby is a full-time duty. It would have been extremely difficult for Anna to manage on her own, I am sure she would have managed, but it would have been entirely unfair on her, after all, the baby is ours, not just hers.

2

GETTING PREPARED TO RAISE A CHILD (PRENATAL)

As soon as Anna and I found out she was pregnant with Ella, I went into extreme planning mode, after celebrating of course. We informed our friends and family about our good news, celebrated some more, and then got down to the real business.

Read as much as you can

There is a lot of material available that allows parents to begin planning and sorting out what they need in order to prepare for their new-born baby. As Dwight D. Eisenhower once said, "Plans are worthless, but planning is essential," which very applies to planning for childhood. While Anna began reading books on her reading list, I began reading the books on my reading list. I was looking to understand how pregnancy works, how I can support my partner, be a good father and caretaker, and how my life will change after our baby arrives. I got hold of a handful of books which provided me with a great understanding and prepared me for what was to come. The type of books I opted for ranged from How-to books to personal experience books. One of my favourites was *The Expectant Father* by Armin Brott and Jennifer Ash. Just make sure you read the latest edition if you do end up buying it. Moreover, there is a wide range of material available online, from personal blogs to official papers.

Honestly speaking, when I first began to read the books on my list, it felt daunting and I wondered if I would be able to do everything the books advised or retain all the knowledge it was throwing out at me. There were times when I would read a page and put it down in frustration because it made me feel overwhelmed. Sometimes, if I liked a particular book more, I would re-read it and visualize myself doing what I was reading, which made it easier for me to retain all the new information. However, eventually, my anxiety decreased and I actually started enjoying the content. There was so much I did not know about pregnancy, childbirth, and child-rearing, I felt as if I had unlocked a whole new world. Plus, researching myself proved beneficial in the long run for Anna and I. I was not pestering her constantly to explain things to me or she did not have to sit me down and explain how things worked. It is a small amount of effort you are putting in for a great return.

Watch videos

What helped me further was watching informative videos and listening to audiobooks as well. If you are not a book person, videos may work for you. They are more interactive and will keep you engaged. While reading is great, I feel watching videos allows me to understand the technical know-how more easily. I tend to understand things better when I can view them visually hence, I enjoyed watching videos more. I learned how to assemble a baby cot by watching, how to install the baby car seat, how to change diapers (yes, I did that), how to swaddle a baby, and how to burp a baby all through videos. Additionally, videos are not hard to come by. The Internet has got you covered so make the most of it. You have no excuse to slack here!

Speak to doctors

Another mode of preparation Anna and I thought to be very helpful was speaking to paediatricians. We have a few friends who are paediatricians so we got in touch with them to ask them a few general questions about babies' health. If you have any friends or family who happen to be doctors, I advise you to do the same. We discovered there are quite a few health concerns a new-

born baby is born with, such as jaundice, skin conditions, feeding, and fever. It is common for new-born
babies to develop skin conditions right after they enter
this world. Fortunately, most of these skin conditions
are short-lived, so there is no need to worry. Jaundice
affects most new-born babies, hence before getting the
mother and the baby are discharged, the hospital staff
checks the jaundice levels of the baby. While jaundice
goes away naturally in some babies, it stays on in some
for a longer period which requires adequate treatment
in the hospital. Moreover, the paediatrician told us to
look out for any signs of jaundice upon our return
home through observing our baby's skin colour and
signs of dehydration – dehydration normally results in
fewer wet diapers. Any serious infection will usually be
indicated through mild to high fever in a new-born
baby or changes in the baby's behavior. If your baby is a
month old, then he/she will have to be taken to the
hospital. One of the major concerns with new-born
babies is feeding and regulating their feeding patterns.
The paediatrician said new-born babies feed every one-
and-half- to three hours in the first few days and it
takes around three to four weeks to establish a set
routine. Moreover, an indicator of your baby being fed
enough is if six or more diapers are changed in a day
and if two yellowish bowel movements are passed.
Moreover, after the baby is fed, they will usually spit

up, mostly accompanied by a burp. If your baby does vomit consistently after feeding, take them to the hospital. Lastly, do not worry about weight loss in the first 10 to 14 days, they go back to their original birth weight within the first two weeks. These tips proved really helpful to Anna and I and our mind were put at ease. Usually, new parents go into a frenzy, rightfully so, if their baby is not adhering to what is considered normal or healthy. Thus, if you know the basics of new-born babies' health, it will allow you to navigate the initial days at home in a calmer and more knowing manner. I also felt slightly more informed because I accompanied Anna to as many doctor's appointments as I possibly could. Routine checks do not just help you be more in sync with the pregnancy but they also allow you to raise any concerns or questions you may have. While I do have a demanding job at an accounting firm, I managed to make it to most appointments because Anna created a schedule that allowed me to be there as much as possible.

Attend birthing and parenting classes

The next agenda on my preparation list was birthing classes. These classes are important in preparing, not only for the mother but for the father as well. Truth be told, I was hesitant at first because I had a fear of being the only father at the birthing classes we had signed up for, but I realized I was doing it for myself, my wife, and our baby, and the fear disappeared itself. By the time the classes were wrapping up, I found myself relieved that I came across numerous men like myself who shared the same worries and concerns as I did.

I believe parenting solely focuses on motherhood and the mother doing everything, which is unfair, to say the least. The father has an equal role and must take responsibility beyond impregnating. Birthing classes provide parents to be with information on labour, the process of birth, choices about pain relief, how a husband can support his wife or partner through the entire process of giving birth, parenting and the challenges in the initial months and breastfeeding (which is the mother's area of expertise, but it helps to be informed about the process). Birthing classes also provide you with the golden opportunities to ask all the questions you have got on your mind, to get advice, and speak to other parents as well. For me, my first birthing class was extremely nerve-racking and exciting as well. I was one of those eager students who wanted to sit in the front row, ask all the questions and soak in all the information that was being given out. While Anna thought it was cute, I am sure the other fathers in the class did not think so. I made some great friends during these birthing classes. Since they were in the same stage as I was, I was able to connect with them more easily and they seemed more relatable than most of my friends. Do not get me wrong, I love my friends, though they are all in different stages of parenthood, hence I found it relieving that I could talk to expecting fathers and share our stories and concerns. Knowing that there were so many more fathers-to-be like I was felt comforting, I was not the only one who was excited yet nervous, happy yet anxious.

I believe birthing classes helped Anna and I work better as a team through the entire pregnancy, up until the moment she gave birth. Since I had attended all the classes with her, I knew what to expect, be more confident and supportive during each stage of labour. Moreover, what I learned in the classes gave me the confidence to deal with all the new issues and challenges when we returned home with Ella. Rather than being a deer caught in headlights, I was on my A-game. You do not have to go much further than your local hospital to find out about birthing classes. If you search online, you will be able to find a list of birthing classes there as well. Anna and I picked the weekend classes because I was able to attend them. Decide which classes suit your partner and you best and then figure out what day works for you two. If you want to be entirely involved, I suggest you opt for the weekend classes, that way work does not overlap with the birthing classes.

While I was finding out about birthing classes at our hospital, I came across antenatal classes just for men, which I did not know existed up until that moment. Did you know? Such classes are run solely by men who are also fathers for men who are becoming fathers. Being the eager beaver that I am, I signed up for these as well. If you are wondering how I managed to attend these as well as the ones with Anna, I can let you in on the secret. I took them one after the other, so it was more convenient for me. While it did get tiring at most times, it was fruitful. At the men-only classes, I figured out the type of father I wanted to be and what I expected from myself and Anna on this journey. A lot of introspection was required from my end. I was able to learn more about ways of interacting with our baby and how to be more involved in taking care of the baby and its needs. One of the main differences between the men-only and joint birthing classes was that, issues such as the impact of having a baby on a relationship, money matters, sex, and postnatal depression were discussed. These classes were easy going and I always had a good laugh during them, made some great friends, and learned valuable lessons. If you do not have time to do both, it is entirely alright. You can opt to attend one and if you have a clashing appointment that cannot be missed on the day of the class, you can ask your partner to fill you in on what was taught.

Speaking to new parents and experienced parents

By the time Anna and I decided to try for a baby, a lot of our friends and family were already parents. This worked out in my favor because I got the chance to ask my friends and family members a lot of questions I had on my mind. Remember my best friend who rushed out of a Lakers game on a Saturday night to tend to his baby? Well, he became my go-to person for all my father-related queries. He took me to a couple of play-dates with his group of dad friends and I noticed how so many fathers seemed natural at what they were doing. Those occasions actually helped me calm the fear I had of not being a good enough father. It is a terrifying thought and I keep on reiterating this statement only because I want you to know you are not alone in feeling the way you are. Socializing with other dads turned out to be quite helpful. Being around fathers helped me get a perspective on how different men are as fathers as well as gave me a real-time chance at viewing how to handle children.

I had had a rough and long day at work because I was juggling between office work and speaking to builders and contractors about the nursery room for Ella. Anna wasn't having the best of days at home either. When I got home, I just wanted to watch some Netflix, have pizza and spend time with Anna, but Anna's mom and sister were gone. While I was slightly annoyed that I could not enjoy my private time with Anna, I also realized we both could use our own space. So, I decided to meet my group of dad friends which turned out to be a massive mood lifter for me. If you do find yourself overwhelmed beyond belief or mentally and physically exhausted throughout the journey and you do not want to burden your pregnant wife, the group of dad friends is a really great place to unwind and vent your emotions. I found myself doing that and they offered me open space to talk about my feelings without being judged. What's more, they gave me reassurance and I actually felt better after speaking to them. Anna and I have a great understanding between us, but there were moments throughout the journey where I felt Anna had a lot going on herself, hence I turned to my 'Dads' friends quite a bit.

Paternity leave time

Since our pregnancy was planned, I had requested the Human Resources (HR) department at my office well in advance about my paternity leave. California is one of the few states that allow and offers a form of paid family leave. Through this program, an employee can get up to six weeks of paid leave and receive 55% of their salary. I had opted to take off 12 weeks and was getting half my salary for six weeks so it worked out well for me. There is a misconception that paternity leave is a mini-vacation, reality check – it certainly is not. I believe it helped me immensely, not only in terms of providing physical and emotional help to Anna, but also bonding with Ella in her first few months. Before I spoke to the HR department, Anna and I sat together and decided on a few important factors which you can take into consideration as well. One of the first things to do while planning paternity leave is;

1. Plan in advance. This works out in your favor as well as your office's favor. Inform your office once you have confirmed when you are planning to utilize your paternity paid leave. Moreover, if you plan your paternity leave in

advance, it allows you to save up on leaves accordingly.

2. Figure out shifts between yourself and your partner. Most parents take maternity and paternity leave together and some even alternate their leaves. You and your partner need to decide what works best for you two – financially, emotionally, and personally.

3. Find out your office policy on paternity leave.

Making our home baby proof

One of the things Anna was most excited about was planning Ella's nursery. I started feeding off Anna's nesting vibes and both of us went into a deep planning and baby proof mode. As exciting as it sounds, it is a long and tiresome, as well as costly project to undertake, but one that needs to be regardless. To begin with, I conducted a safety test for our house. What does that mean you ask? Well, I wanted to see how safe our house is for our baby. Even though Ella would not be crawling around till around six months, I wanted to be as prepared as I could be rather than leaving things till the last minute. While it was difficult to manage a home improvement and revamp project, it was also fulfilling to know that Ella would have a safe space to move around in.

Moreover, preparing for a child takes effort and time, so the word weekends disappeared from my life. Now my weekends mostly revolved around birthing classes, doctor's appointments, and home projects. Gone was the 28-year-old drinking beer at a bar on a Saturday night – he was replaced by super dad-to-be (me). It is time-consuming, yes, but it is doable. At times I felt stretched beyond my means and there were moments where I wanted to give up, which is okay. We are human after all, make sure to give yourself the space to relax as well. Back to the house safety test. To begin with,

294 | ALFIE THOMAS

1. Conduct a home safety test.

- If you have any arms and ammunition at home, please unload the arms, lock the arms and ammunition separately in a cupboard and store the keys in a place known only to you. Install smoke detectors in the house.
- Store products such as dishwasher pods, medicines, detergent, soap dishes out of the child's reach.
- Install sturdy baby height structures.
- Install gates on stairways and any exit or entry point.
- Install electrical outlet covers.
- Put edge bumpers on furniture with sharp edges.
- Install a lid lock on your toilet.
- Conceal any wires and cords and make use of cord holders.
- View things from the baby's perspective. Get down on all fours in order to see things you may not see standing up.

2. Prepare your house for overnight visitors.

If you and your partner are expecting any overnight visitors once your baby is born, prepare your home for them. Have the towels, sheets, and toiletries ready for them. Once I returned to work after my paternity leave ended, Anna's mother moved in for a couple of weeks to help Anna with Ella. Being prepared beforehand really saved us from running around last minute with Ella and getting the guest room ready for my mother-in-law.

3. Spring clean the house

- Before starting your cleaning frenzy, make sure you wear gloves, and if your wife is helping you clean make sure she definitely wears gloves because pregnancy causes the skin to become sensitive. Since cleaning products have chemicals in them, it is best to keep your skin protected.
- Open all the windows in your house (if you live in a colder area, keep them open if it is not too cold). Keeping windows allow for ventilation and air circulation which improves the air quality within the house.
- Start cleaning knobs, switches, handles, the kitchen counter, the kitchen sink, basically anything you touch on a regular basis. These areas tend to gather germs because we use them more frequently.

- Dust the home a couple of times before the baby arrives home. Dust allergies are the last thing you want your new-born baby to develop.
- Clean in areas where you will not think of. Hence, any gaps in your sofas, or behind the bed and above the shelf. Make sure you dust these areas.
- When we began cleaning, we came up with a rule where we would leave our shoes at the front door so as not to get in bacteria into the house. We installed a shoe shelf in the entrance area and told our guests to do the same.

4. Reimagine your space with baby belongings

Anna and I love how we did up our house. We hand-picked each and everything to make it what it was. However, once we found out Anna was pregnant with Ella, we began to view our space with a baby in mind. We began to make space for our baby in the kitchen as well. How so? I emptied out a couple of drawers where we would place Ella's bottles, Sippy cups, and her baby cutlery and crockery. Moreover, clean out your fridge and make space to put breast milk and formula. I placed a few cloth bags around the house, for Ella's toys and any extra clothes we could need. It makes everything neater and more accessible.

5. Designing Ella's nursery

We picked lilac and cream as a colour theme for Ella's room. Anna and I spent a lot of time on *Pinterest* creating mood boards and playing around with a lot of textures and palettes till we found the perfect one. It was an exciting project, but time-consuming nonetheless. Yet again, if you are wondering how I managed to take this project on, the secret is utilizing your weekends for these and asking for help from your friends and family. There are some essentials you will need to pick for the nursery;

- Cot
- Bedding
- Changing table
- Dresser
- Storage baskets
- A baby mobile
- Rocking chair or armchair for adults
- Clothes hamper
- A baby monitor
- Nightlight
- Bluetooth speaker
- Baskets for toys
- Shelves for storage
- Ceiling fan

An important tip Anna's sister gave us was to leave space for the room to grow, which turned out to be very handy over the years. The tip is to think long-term – the cot will be replaced by a toddler-sized bed in a few years, more shelves may be added, and so on. Another tip to adhere to (if you are looking to save money and time) is to buy a cot you can turn into a toddler size bed when the child grows up. There are quite a few options available in the stores and they come with a manual so it is easy to figure out.

While you are baby-proofing the house, remember to baby-proof the nursery as well. The nursery turned out to be lovely once it was complete. It was definitely

Pinterest-worthy. While aesthetics matter, remember to keep comfort in mind because you will be spending a lot of time in the nursery as well.

3

THE IMPORTANCE OF A FATHER IN RAISING A CHILD (0-3 MONTHS)

W hen my siblings and I were born, I remember my mother being the primary and sole caregiver. Yes, my father was around on the weekends and on our birthdays, however, my father was not expected to help around the house or help my mother with child-rearing. That was a given. Financially supporting the family was the only prerogative. The family system and expectations were quite orthodox. Now that I am a father and I can witness parenthood first-hand, I am in awe of my mother. I cannot even begin to think how she managed to raise three siblings by herself. Personally, I would have had a nervous breakdown. The need to be there for my wife and child does not necessarily emanate from the narrative changing in the 21st century, more so, it stems from my basic need of being there for them and with them because I want to. Fortunately, times have changed, there is more awareness and the discourse slowly began to evolve in order for the husband to be more involved in child-rearing. Being involved in child-rearing has multiple benefits; you are more involved in your child's life which aids the emotional development of your child, you get to develop a deeper bond with your new-born baby, you are able to support your wife emotionally and physically and you get the chance to be more proactive in the formative years of your child. It is a win-win situation. While researching and reading up during Anna's prenatal phase, I came across a quote by Kent Nürburg which really resonated with me, "It is much easier to become a father than to be one." I couldn't agree more. The real challenges begin when you take on responsibility for bringing a human into this world.

Benefits of early involvement in your baby's life

Your involvement with the process predates when you find out your partner is pregnant and when you start preparing for your child in the prenatal time period. I have been involved since I found out Anna was pregnant, as you must have figured out by now. Due to the fact that I had taken paternity leave for 12 weeks, I was able to be more wholly involved with Ella's first three months. The first three months went by within the blink of an eye, except for the days on which I was running low on sleep. My best friend – coffee – helped me get through those nights. It has been found that fathers who are more responsive to their baby's cry, fathers who hold, cuddle, and hug them more often and take care of their needs such as changing diapers and feeding them, have a positive effect on the child's self-confidence and behavior over time. As Sigmund Freud said "I cannot think of any need in childhood as strong as the need for a father's protection," and I cannot agree more.

Moreover, studies have proven that children whose fathers are more proactive during their infancy are less likely to show mental health symptoms later on in their childhood. For me, fatherhood is about loving Ella, teaching her and playing with her, setting limits, and being her role model. This unique and powerful role of mine began early on in Anna's prenatal stage. When fathers are involved in the prenatal time, providing the mother with help and support, they are bound to help later on as well according to research. The relationship is important for healthy development in all domains, including physical, social, emotional, and thinking skills. From birth, the father's involvement in the baby's caregiving contributes to high levels of secure attachment for the baby which becomes the vital foundation of a loving bond between both parents and their child over time. Children whose fathers are more involved in daily care, feeding, bathing, and playing with them tend to be more confident and motivated as they grow older, they even enjoy more social connections with their peers which strengthens their social and emotional competency. They also tend to be more patient and later on can handle the stresses and frustrations associated with schooling more easily than children with less involved fathers.

Research also shows these children are also less likely to get into trouble at home, school, or in the neighbourhood and less likely to experience depression. Those fathers who help, care for, nurture, and play with their babies end up raising children who perform better at school and develop better language and cognitive skills. The time dads devote to children really matters. Research shows that the more time fathers spend on enriching play with their child, such as pretend games and sharing stories, the better that child's math and reading scores are at ages 10 and 11. Involved fathers also support their children's communication skills. Fathers tend to ask more questions than mothers which builds their vocabulary and conversational skills. The benefits of early involvement also extend to physical benefits. Dads make a difference in the physical area because they tend to play more active tumble games with their children, which builds large muscle groups. This type of play also helps children regulate their emotions and bodies. It is not just the father-child relationship that benefits from your involvement – relations between parents matter too. Husbands and wives who feel satisfied in their relationships tend to be more responsive, affectionate, and confident when caring for their babies and show more self-control when dealing with defiant toddlers. Fathers who are involved in their baby's life – tending to them and playing with them – tend to experience less conflict with mothers, which also strengthens the adult relationship. The everyday moments you are living with your partner and baby help build a strong bond.

Effects of a father's absence from a child's life

While there are multifold benefits to you being involved, I would also like to show you the dark side of not being involved in your child's life. Children who grow up without their father or whose fathers leave are more likely to suffer from behavioral problems, drop out of school, suffer from depression and mental health issues, have financial problems, have problems with anger and aggression, and get into the habit of unhealthy intoxicants. Moreover, if you are an uninvolved father, that has consequences as well.

Your child may be more anxious, emotionally withdrawn, fearful of becoming dependent on others, and more vulnerable. Research demonstrates that children with uninvolved fathers display shortfalls in emotional, social, cognition, and attachment skills. Moreover, they tend to perform below par in all aspects of life. Children emulate what they see their parents do and the type of love and care they receive. Hence, children who have uninvolved parents or an uninvolved mother/father will have difficulty in developing attachments in their later years, which can also lead to avoiding intimacy in adult relationships. According to scientific research, fathers undergo neurogenesis during the first few days after the birth of their child and also go through the process of creating and establishing a biochemical bond between themselves and their child. Neurogenesis is a process whereby more neurons are developed by the brain in order to adapt and readapt according to the situations we find ourselves in. Neurogenesis is also connected to learning new things in life, hence by learning new things we have the power to grow more neurons. What's more, is that this process also affects the new-born baby. The new-born baby is actually expecting the aforementioned bond to be established, to begin with. Miracles of nature!

In the future, children who were solely reared by mothers showed higher occurrences of emotional and psychological issues, more aggression, an increased incidence of addiction problems, and more likely to find themselves in trouble.

Sense of fulfillment

To be honest, it was not these effects and benefits that prompted me to be there for Anna and Ella, it was my personal need and want. Yes, I became more aware of how my presence can benefit Ella and that did play a part in me being more actively involved, but I knew I wanted to be the best father to Ella when I found out Anna was pregnant. It was an innate feeling. There were moments when I would be dejected and exhausted beyond belief, but one smile or giggle from Ella would uplift my mood. When I would hear such anecdotes from new fathers I would scoff internally and think it to be a fluff story, because how can a smile from a baby really change one's mood so drastically? I thought new parents were boring and their obsession with their new-born was overwhelming – sounds harsh, I know. It took my personal experience to realize it, and I know when the time comes to relate this story to fathers-to-be, they will most likely be scoffing internally at me as well. I became the exact same type of father I would make fun of. I think it was God's way of having a good laugh at my cost.

I believe babies have the power to make you happy and deal with stress more effectively. I had had a long and tough day at work. A meeting with a client did not go well, hence I returned home in a foul mood, not wanting to interact with anyone and wanting to watch mindless TV and go to sleep. However, when I returned home I was hit with the realization that I am a father now. My stress coping mechanism was very different when I was not a father. Parenting is such a massive task that one automatically puts their emotions in the backseat to look after the needs and wants of your baby. I am not advocating that repression is a good coping mechanism all the time, however, it becomes the need of the hour when your baby's needs are more urgent than yours. Hence, when I returned home and saw Anna feeding Ella, I realized I did not have to but wanted to put my bad mood aside and take over from Anna and look after Ella myself. And at that moment, Ella was the perfect antidote to my bad mood. Instead of moping around, I found myself feeding Ella and playing hours of peek-a-boo. Her constant surprise and laughter cheered me up automatically. I made a mental note to thank Ella in the future for being my dose of happiness on days when I needed it the most. When your days are filled with sadness, a baby can give you a sense of purpose and a reason to be happy. Ella and Anna have been my safe haven for so many days where I thought it was just me against the world.

The importance of paternity leave

Taking paternity leave is imperative for the well-being of your family. It is the beginning of developing a relationship between the father and the newborn baby and you need time to do that. Moreover, paternity leave also reiterates the belief that fathers are not just there to provide financially, but also as caretakers and an integral component of the family. For fathers, it is important to have them be present and active as soon as possible because it allows fathers to be networked into how the new family runs, works, and interacts right off the bat and then networking grows and increases over time. It might not work as effectively if the father enters the child's life at 5, 10, or 15-years of age. The first year after a baby is born is critical for the couple, especially if it is the first child. The best way to strengthen your relationship during this time is to invest your time and effort into fatherhood. Moreover, when new fathers take paternity leave, they are able to take that time to understand what kind of father they will be to their child and what kind of partner they will be after their family grows. Usually, our ideas of fatherhood are developed from seeing our fathers, seeing fathers on TV, or reading about fathers, however, spending time with your child will help you understand exactly the type of father you can and want to be. It is easier to learn to parent when your partner is around as well. Research indicates that there is a strong correlation between fathers taking paternity leave and marital stability

Taking paternity leave allows you to contribute to your child's development. There is evidence that dads usually talk in louder voices as compared to mothers and use more complex language when they communicate with infants and that turns out to be an important predictor of speech and language development and eventually academic readiness. Even the way fathers socialize and play with their children is unique and that promotes important social skills development, hence when children eventually grow up and enter a preschool setting they are equipped with tools to negotiate with socially complex interactions that happen with their peers. Later on in life when school starts, the father's emphasis on academic skill-building makes unique contributions to the child's eventual academic achievements and success which predicts long-term positive outcomes in the child's personal life and is a positive contribution to society as well. For fathers, their identity as a father will change positively if they are able to take on a more active hands-on role and contribute to caretaking tasks. In terms of benefits for the family unit, paternity leave establishes an upward and positive family trajectory.

Moreover, paternity leave helps build a new father's confidence. How so? Well, the only way to learn to parent is to throw yourself into it and practice and learn on the job. This in turn will help in developing confidence in making choices and doing tasks centered on your child. Once you do the task at hand and succeed at it, you will be more confident doing it again next time, such as changing diapers, feeding the baby, and burping the baby.

One of the biggest fears of taking paternity leave is hurting your career. I can say this from personal experience. Being in an accounting firm is not easy, it is a competitive environment. I was worried that I would miss out on any promotion opportunities or would start lagging at work upon my return. And I am not the only one who had this fear. During my numerous conversations with new and experienced fathers, a lot of them voiced this concern as well. However, during the time I was reading and researching on pregnancy and parenthood, research indicated the opposite of what I feared. Men who take on a more equal part in caregiving and taking paternity leave are actually much happier and satisfied with their jobs. I can vouch for these findings because when I eventually returned to work, I did actually feel happier rather than feeling what I had initially feared. This in turn benefits the employer. There is actual research on the effect parental leaves have on employees. According to the research, three-fourth of employees are most likely to stay with their employer due to the flexibility and allowance of parental leaves they are offered by the organization. These organizations also highlight increased rates of retaining employees as well as more engagement. Moreover, employees return with a happier and motivated attitude. Hence, paternity leave should be equally important at organizational levels as well. Paternity leave also promotes gender equality in the workplace. By allowing paternity leave, the organization is promoting a culture of celebrating women and helping them progress. How so? By allowing paternity leave, the organization is essentially enabling the father to be there for his wife and child and act as a support system. It is only fair to give a male employee paternity leave in order to be more active at home with his new family.

Breaking the gender norms

Parenting is synonymous with the mother doing everything possible for the child. Yes, pregnancy is a female-related realm, but that does not mean we shirk away from the other responsibilities that surround it. Moreover, mothers are half of the equation of what constitutes a conventional and heterosexual couple in society. Earlier on, society was complacent with the idea that men were redundant when it came to the process of child-rearing and upbringing. However, society dictates a different narrative now, mostly backed by science. Who are we to prove science wrong?

Let us forget science for a few minutes as well, is it not just a natural urge to be there for your child and wife? Does the need have to arise from scientific or emotional benefits? Fathers are not merely background props who only provide financially. This harmful stereotype has propagated a generation of absent fathers and that is not right. I come from a similar family; thus I have the first-hand experience of how it is to be in a family where the mother is the sole caregiver. Fathers do have an enormous effect on their children. So much so that when fathers are depressed or stressed, their children get as socially, emotionally, and behaviourally affected by it as they would with their mothers. That says a lot about the importance of a father's presence in his child's life. This argument goes beyond gender norms and their impact on children because research suggests that there are no gender differences in the impact of a father's parenting stress on the cognitive development of a child.

Changing the definition of parenthood in society and amongst individuals is imperative. It is assumed that loving and caring for children is a feminine need and urge and it comes naturally to them. Except, it is not entirely true. This idea has harmful implications on the concept of parenthood as well as what we pass on as the accepted norm from generation to generation. Furthermore, this idea promotes the norm of men taking the back seat because child-rearing is not their forte and what good can come out of them trying to do a woman's job? It is not a woman's job, just the way a woman wings it as she goes along the process, so should a man. Nobody is born with the inherent skills of looking after a baby, we learn along the way. Moreover, the idea of fathers in our culture promotes fathers being fun and games and not entirely involved in the child-rearing process. When they do help out, it is considered extremely nice and helpful, as if they are going the extra mile to do what is actually required of them. While I was growing up, I would notice how much appreciation my uncle would receive when he would babysit his own children, as if he was doing something extraordinary. Whereas when my aunty would do the same, it would go unnoticed, because that was what she was meant to do.

Historically this idea worked. A world where women were confined to one job – procreating and men were confined to one job – breadwinners. This narrative is obsolete in developed countries, though it still holds a lot of importance in a lot of parts of the world. However, as society evolves, so do ideas and concepts. Hence, holding one parent accountable for the well-being of the child is wrong. Moreover, we need to think about how our behaviour is setting a precedent for our children. I know I do not want Ella to internalize these fallacies as she grows up. She needs to see what a healthy functioning family looks like, one that divides the responsibility of parenthood between the mothers and fathers.

4

THE FIRST FEW MONTHS AT HOME WITH ELLA (0-6 MONTHS)

B ringing a new-born baby home is a special time for parents. You may be wondering what happens next. Reality kicks in! It is a daunting time for parents and it is scary as well. Ella relied on us for everything so there was barely any room for error. However, while it may be challenging, it is also a beautiful time; remember to soak in all the new memories with your new-born baby because they grow up really fast. A lot of people told us to kiss our freedom goodbye, while that was true, it is also a temporary period. Get into child-rearing with realistic expectations and understand it will be difficult; we do a disservice by not talking about the reality of it more openly.

The challenges, memories, and art of reshuffling priorities

Since I had taken a three-month paternity leave from work, I was at home with Anna and Ella. I do not know if you can tell by now, but I am extremely organized and love making lists. I enjoy having a routine and sticking to it. Life before Ella was very different in the sense that Anna and I had time to do more things. However, after Ella, I had to reset my routine and to-do list expectations because I would be unable to find time to do the things I had planned for the day. I would recommend that you take your to-do list and dedicate half of the list to just taking care of the new-born baby. Some days nothing but taking care of your baby is accomplished and that is okay because you are entirely responsible for your baby.

It was the first weekend with Ella at home and I had planned out an ambitious day which included going to the gym, spending time with Ella and Anna, catching up on a show, and meeting friends at night. In retrospect, I cannot help but laugh at myself. For a single man, this is like a regular and doable day, but for a father with a new-born baby, it is quite an ambitious plan. Good on you if you manage to do this, you are most probably superhuman. I did accomplish going to the gym, but the rest of the day was spent taking care of Ella. I eventually did not get time to watch my show and ended up cancelling on my friends. Funnily enough, they knew I was going to bail on them.

It took me a while to resettle into my new routine, which was mostly Anna and I alternating taking care of Ella. However, we also took out time to do what was possible in the window of time we got to ourselves. Remember, self-care is vital for your well-being.

Even stepping out of the house with a new-born can be challenging the first few times. It was daunting for me. Anna had to meet her friends and I was heading out to do the groceries so I decided to take Ella with me. Bad idea. Midway Ella began crying uncontrollably. I had to actually cut my trip short and head home. I fed her with Anna's pumped breast milk and swayed her to sleep. I was aware going grocery shopping was pretty ambitious with a new-born baby. But that is how I learned what not to do the next time I take Ella out alone. After that, I planned my next few outings to be light and easy, such as a walk in the park, sauntering through the aisles at a grocery store, and grabbing a coffee with a friend. These things were easy to escape and I got to test out how Ella settles in such situations. By doing this, you will get to know your baby better, what time of the day is better suited to them and how much time you can take while you are out. Remember, things like this come with experience so take it easy. Your first outing will be nerve-wracking, as was mine, but once you start, it will get easier and you will become an expert over time. When I took Ella for a walk in the park, it was a whole new experience for me. Walking around with her in the stroller was a different kind of fun. I used to park her stroller near a bench, take her in my lap and sit with her on the bench and watch people walking by. Birds chirping around us, Ella smiling and moving her cherubic arms around, people smiling and waving at Ella – I do not think I have ever had such peaceful and wholesome moments before in my life. Walks in the park with Ella soon became a form of exercise and a way of bonding with her over her initial years.

A valuable piece of advice I would like to offer to you is to teach your new-born early on to love their crib. It may be easier to have them fall asleep in your arms now and it may feel heart-warming and perfect, but it will get difficult for you down the road as a parent. It takes some time to get your new-born into this routine so give it time and be patient. As it is, the first three-month sleep schedule is not easy. The trick is to put your baby down in the crib when they are sleepy and not asleep because you have to train them on how to fall asleep by themselves in their crib. When your wife or you are nursing your baby, make sure they do not fall asleep while nursing. It makes it easier if you think through the perspective of the baby. If you are nursing your baby, he/she falls asleep in your arms and they wake up in an entirely different place, they will naturally cry – as would adults, if not cry, but be startled. It took Anna and me a while to build a night-time routine for Ella, we eventually succeeded. Anna would nurse Ella and then I would read a story and then put her to sleep in her crib. It definitely did not work right off the bat, there were moments where Ella would start crying when we would try to put her to sleep in her crib, but we were patient and we managed. There were moments when Anna would fall asleep and I would tip-toe over to Ella's crib just to see if she was sleeping sound. There were nights where I would find her wide awake, looking around in amazement with her big deep blue eyes, and then there would be nights where she would be sleeping peacefully. I know it sounds cliché, but seeing her in those moments filled my heart with a love I had not felt before. But along with those beautiful and wholesome feelings, there were days when Anna and I would be running on two to three hours of sleep, had not eaten a proper meal, and had not taken a shower longer than two minutes. Those were the days when I felt I was stretched to my limit and I think I can say the same for Anna. The feeling did not leave me feeling bitter or angry, it was more a feeling of being exhausted and needing a break. When it comes to sleep, the harsh reality is that you will definitely be sleep-deprived. So tell yourself sleep is overrated and for a short amount of time, you will be sleep-deprived. Come to terms with this reality. You and your partner may be waking up every hour to feed the baby or the check on the baby. Since babies grow rapidly, they need constant nourishment. Here is a fun fact for you; babies sleep 16 hours out of 24 hours in a day but never when we really want them to. By three months most babies can sleep through the night and it will feel like heaven when they do that.

Crying is the only way a baby can communicate with you and when they cry it usually means they are hungry, tired, need a diaper change, in pain, or over-stimulated. You will learn how to respond adequately to their cries over time. Expect your new-born baby to cry four hours (minimum) out of 24 hours in a day. This may not be consecutive crying but it definitely feels like that. They also cry more during evening hours and want to usually eat between 6 pm and 1 am when you are most exhausted. Of course, this can be frustrating but it is a part of the process. Hence it is important to build your routine around your baby's routine. There will be a lot of reshuffling, a lot of cancelled plans, missed appointments, sleepless nights, but the good news is that it is manageable.

Luckily, Anna and I had hired house help, so she managed the daily chores for us. Moreover, we had a strong support system in our family and friends. Anna's mother and my mother were our saving grace. Our friends stepped in to help from time to time, whenever we asked them. So please do not be afraid to ask for help and support whenever you need it, and please believe me when I say you really will need it.

How my relationship with Anna changed after we had Ella

Having a baby changes one's life and will change your relationship as well. You will learn to adjust to new norms and life will not be the same and that is not a bad thing necessarily.

Anna and I dated for a year, fell in love, and then got married. You may have heard that it is easier to fall in love and more difficult to stay in love and keep your relationship nourished and growing. Well, it is true. Your marriage will not work on autopilot mode and if you leave it at that, you will be setting the ground for an imminent crash.

Anna is the yin to my yang and we get each other. While we have had our fair share of arguments and fights, we have worked through them in a mature and adult manner. The one thing that really helped us individually and together as a couple was personal therapy. There were epiphanies during my sessions that really changed my outlook on a lot of things. One of the things that really resonated with me was self-love.

Did it ever cross your mind that how you feel about yourself could go a long way in deciding the fate of your relationship? Self-love is the biggest contributor to happiness and marriage. How do you practice self-love? It is simple. Trust yourself to make good decisions, allow yourself to feel your emotions, minus the harsh judgment, and treat yourself as valuable (do not confuse that with arrogance). Self-love is about having a sense of self-sufficiency without tying your happiness and sense of self-worth to someone else. So go ahead, build and flex your self-love muscle and take good care of your well-being to build a happier narrative of your life.

Anna and I felt we were in a stable position in our marriage and were emotionally, physically, and financially ready to start a family. Having a baby strains relationships in a lot of ways, so please be sure you and your partner are in a good place before you two decide to take such a big step.

One of the biggest issues we dealt with was Anna's postpartum depression. Hormones play a role in how a woman feels after she gives birth to her baby. Oestrogen and progesterone are two hormones that help support a woman's pregnancy and these levels decline after delivery. Hence between day five and 14 after the baby's delivery women will feel the effect of this. These hormones combined with stress hormones (which are in abundance since new mothers are pretty stressed about everything from their health to their baby's health) actually cause chemical changes in the brain that affect the mood. There were days where Anna would cry without a reason, be irritable, on edge, which was completely normal. At first, I was really overwhelmed and did not know how to pacify her or make it better for her, however, I asked her what she needed from me and what I could do for her. Our communication was centred on our emotional needs a lot during this time. Postpartum blues are extremely common, around 80% or more experience these feelings within the first six weeks of delivery. It is very real!

It can onset at any point during the first year of the baby's life.

There were times when Anna would stop taking care of herself and would withdraw from friends and family. It was not constant, but it was present. I gave it my best in terms of patience, giving her space, and supporting her. Build a healthy and constructive narrative around postpartum depression with your partner. Fortunately for Anna, she was also seeing her therapist, which helped her during the process.

Male postpartum depression is a big deal. I went through a depressive phase as well. Fathers are immune to depression too. Around 7% of fathers suffer from clinical depression within the first three months of a baby's life and the number reaches 10% higher down the road; between six and 12 months. It was a tough period for Anna and me in dealing with our own emotions, but we gave each other space, time, and patience. It is easy to go to the opposite end and bicker, fight and get even more upset so it is important to be mindful during this time. You can be each other's best ally or worst enemy through this adjustment phase. If a woman has depression, then her partner is more likely to be depressed and vice versa. Hence, be open with your feelings, help each other out and be there for each other.

There are some factors that increase the risk of you having male postpartum depression; lack of sleep, financial stress, and relationship stress, history of depression, family history of depression, smoking, and a poor diet. How do you know you have it versus just feeling low? The main difference is that you just cannot get out of it and you feel stuck. More often than not, you will feel sad or hopeless, have a lot of anger and irritability you cannot get over, you do not care to do activities you used to enjoy, there is a big change in your weight, you are always feeling tired and lacking energy and if you are having thoughts of death. You are not alone in this and you can get through it. Following are a few tips that can help you process and work through your male postpartum depression;

- Please get some sleep. You have to make sleep a priority
- Feed your body well. What you put into your body has an effect on how you feel, hence be sure you are eating healthy.
- Reduce alcohol consumption. It helps you feel better physically and emotionally. Let go of that beer you have been craving and see how you feel after.
- Fill your mind with positive messages and focus on uplifting messages. You will have to do this every day.
- See your therapist and speak to him/her about how you are feeling and how you can work through this period.

Another issue Anna and I experienced was that we had sex less often, our conversations were very to the point and we would snap at each other more easily (please do not take it personally every time that happens). While women should not have sex for around six weeks after the delivery, it is up to them when they feel they are ready. When there is so much going on, sex is the last thing on a couple's mind. Sex and intimacy can be difficult for new parents because they will be exhausted, women are going through hormonal changes, and sleep trumps being intimate a lot of times. This did not mean

Anna and I loved each other less or were not attracted to each other anymore. It was the reality of the situation. We had to make more of an effort to get into an intimate mood after having Ella.

I did go through some periods where I felt Anna and I had different levels of sexual desire, there were days where I felt rejected and there were days she felt unwanted and that is natural. Yet again, because Anna and I have great communication and comprehensive skills, we were able to get our feelings across. Instead of having spontaneous sex, we would now plan when to have sex, which seemed really odd and funny at first, but it really helped us out. When we planned in advance it added an element of excitement as well, as if it was a date. On our first planned date, both of us actually got dressed and put to look good for the other, which is another way of conveying how much we care about each other.

Make a mindful effort of spending time with each other. It is a challenge initially, however you can start off small. Go for a walk together, along with the baby in the stroller, have dinner together when you put your baby to sleep, watch a show together, and order in when the baby is asleep. It starts with the small things. Remember to hold hands, hug and cuddle together.

I consider Anna to be quite talkative, as am I, but when Ella was born, our conversations became mere transactions. Our conversations mostly went like "Please hand me her bottle," "I am going to take a shower, stay with Ella," "where is the diaper bag?" I remember one particular day where Anna and I literally only spoke in one-word sentences and when it was time to sleep, I turned to her and said "how was your day?" and we both burst out laughing. Honestly, it was frustrating at first, it was as if constructing an entire sentence that did not focus on Ella was too much effort for both of us. However, this was something we were aware of and tried to make an effort at adjusting. This is where our walks and dinner dates really came in handy. Over the years, this became a habit, we took out time for each other and it allowed our relationship to remain healthy.

To put it simply, yes, your relationship will change, but change is not always bad.

Challenges Millennials face as new parents

Millennials are the generation born from the '80s till the 2000s. So you can do the math and figure out that there is a huge number of people in the world who are Millennials. Anna and I also fall in this category.

While the generation of baby boomers had their fair share of challenges with child-rearing, Millennials have their different set of issues too. We grew up with technology, screens, and witnessed the invention of numerous technologies while growing up. Accessibility and convenience were easier to gain for us as opposed to the generation of baby boomers.

Since technology is so etched within us and is vital in all our lives, it also trickles down to our children. While I was introduced to WhatsApp in my 20's, Ella will most probably know everything about WhatsApp and be more tech-savvy than us by the time she is five. And that is the hard truth. This can go both ways for Ella and us.

The Internet, along with technology has helped us introduce Ella and keep in touch with relatives who live far away, such as my siblings who live in New York and Brussels. Distance shrinks when we are able to Zoom call or WhatsApp video call with my brother and sister. I want Ella to be able to recognize them because my siblings are an important part of my life. Hence, in this aspect, technology really works out for me.

Since a baby's brain develops over the first two years of their life, it is imperative that they discover their surroundings, experience the sounds, smells, tastes, and sights. It is vital that you play a lot with your child at this time. However, something Anna and I struggle with as new parents are giving into screen time when we feel exasperated and do not know how to placate her. We are aware that too much screen time is not good for children and their developing minds. Hence, we try to find alternatives and sticking to traditional playtime with her. We try to play a lot of imaginary games, take her outdoors, go for walks with her, however sometimes when we are really exhausted, we do give her the iPad for a certain amount of time – yes, I feel guilty about this which is why it happens rarely.

Moreover, if you want to set a healthy precedent for your child in terms of technology and screen time, you have to be very mindful of your relationship with your phone/devices. I am a Twitter geek and keep scrolling for updates every minute. It is just a reflex action. However, with Ella around, I have reduced my personal screen time and check myself more vigilantly when I am physically around Ella. I am not advocating for you to give up on social media and throw your phone in the furthest corner of your house – just be mindful of your personal screen time around your child. Anna and I have understood that our actions and behavior towards our mobiles and devices will pave the way for Ella's perspective in viewing and using technology when her time comes.

Funnily enough, my parents do not understand this concern because they did not have such issues while raising us.

Another issue that Millennial parents face is financing. Yes, it is generally expensive to have and raise a child but it is a known fact that Millennials face more of a disadvantage when it comes to having and raising children as opposed to the baby boomer generation. This has to do with rising costs and stagnant salaries and wages – essentially, we are doing more with less.

Anna and I both have jobs and we began saving as much as we could early on in our marriage. However, after having Ella, our daily expenses and costs increased a lot. We have to consider issues such as daycare when both of us return to our jobs. Yet again, daycare was not an issue back in our parents' generation because the mother stayed home – there was no concept of a career for a woman once a child was born. Nonetheless, trends have changed and more women are in the workforce than they were before. Thus the need for day-cares has increased and because the demand is high, so are costs. Research states that annual average childcare costs are more costly than housing. That leaves a lot of Millennial parents in a conundrum.

As the world becomes more competitive, the additional or discretionary income for each person has significantly reduced. For Millennials who entered the workforce during the recession and economic recovery, the situation is even more difficult. Young adults today are much better prepared than their predecessors in terms of education and skill set. The Millennials today are more likely to have a college degree, or postgraduate qualification and additional skill sets than the generation before them, yet they are still trapped in low-paying jobs and struggle financially.

Research and statistics show that an on average, an 18 to 34-year-old makes $2,000 less with each passing year than young workers did in 1980, according to the Census Bureau. Moreover, if these individuals are unable to find a way to balance work along with raising a family, they are at the risk of being trapped within the vicious cycle of low wages.

Due to the nature of Millennial's college degrees, various young workers are beginning to start families whilst still paying off their student debt. Hence, saving up for their children's college fund could seem like a faraway dream. Due to this reason, numerous Millennials are delaying parenthood until they feel more stable in their financial situation.

Millennials who decide to have children either way, often face challenging schedules and struggle with managing their monthly budgets. Young parents are more likely to go to work earlier as well as leave earlier than people without children.

Similarly, young adults with children are twice more likely to work more or work double shifts to meet increasing expenses. They are also more likely to work late nights to be able to spend time with their children during the day. Despite this, the number of Millennial parents living in poverty is increasing as per studies and reports.

Thus, it is justified to state that Millennials have their share of stark issues when it comes to raising a family, hence please study your financial situation and career before starting a family. It is always better to plan ahead and weigh the pros and cons.

5

STRIKING A WORK AND HOME LIFE BALANCE

Three months of paternity seemed like a lot before Ella entered our lives, however, it whizzed by within the blink of an eye. I do not think any amount of time is enough with a new-born baby. When it was time to return to work, I was a bag of mixed emotions. While I knew I had to resume my 9 to 5 job, I also wished that I could stay at home, spend time with and take care of Ella (of course support Anna as well). Moreover, when you are at home for 12 weeks, you get out of the corporate flow, hence I was also anxious about the transition back into the corporate life – and more so now because I had a larger responsibility at home – Ella. It was overwhelming, to say the least, but humans are adaptable so it took me a week to get readjusted into the office routine.

Following are a few tips for you to be able to prepare yourself with returning to work and balancing your priorities;

Prepare yourself mentally before returning to work

A week or two before returning to work, remind your boss or supervisor that you will be returning. Ask a colleague to fill you in on what has been happening in your department in regard to your work, this will make it easier for you to catch up on everything when you physically return. If you have any meetings to set up, you can do that a couple of days before returning to work. Moreover, now that you are a father, maybe your working pace will change, so do take that into consideration. Rather than diving back into work headfirst, mentally preparing your mind eases the anxiety and warms you up for what you are getting into.

Speak to your partner about new responsibilities

Since you are returning to work, you will not be around physically to help a lot. Hence responsibilities and duties will automatically get reshuffled. It is a good idea to sit with your partner and figure out these new responsibilities and how you two will manage them while you are away at work. Communication and understanding are really great for your relationship because it makes responsibilities and roles clearer. I was unable to be there for Ella during the vast majority of the day, hence I opted to wake up earlier, bathe, feed, and play with Ella before going to work so that I could spend time with her and give Anna some extra hours to sleep.

Setting boundaries at work

The reality is that once you become a father you will not be able to sit around for longer meetings that go into different tangents. Such as colleagues speaking about sports or a new show. Moreover, a lot of meetings are also held after official work hours. While I used to be an active part of these conversations and meetings before, I could not anymore after we had Ella because I would rather choose to spend that time at home with my family and cater to their needs. While it may be difficult to set this boundary and assert yourself, you have to take a stand. Building a healthy narrative around timings is something all employees should advocate for either way. There may be some meetings you cannot miss and you will stay on for occasionally, but setting the tone and the boundary makes it easier for your coworkers to know your timings beforehand.

Most corporate cultures do not take such issues into account and most people will usually hear the following phrases, 'work is work' 'we had children too and managed just fine not being there.' However, this feeds into an archaic notion and stereotype that men need to be at work regardless, and since the mother is the primary caregiver, what is the need of the father to be there. Just be a bit more mindful of what precedent you set.

Dad guilt

I had heard a lot about mom's guilt but I barely heard anything about dad's guilt. Believe me when I say it is a real thing. I missed Ella and Anna, I also felt pretty bad leaving them at home and returning to work. I was fearful that Ella would not be able to recognize me or she would not want to play with me anymore if I did not see her every hour of the day. At the same time, sometimes work felt more peaceful than home and I used to feel guilty for feeling that. But hey, we're all human!

Appreciate the co-workers who did your work when you were on leave

Most times, when we are on paternity leave, we tend to forget that our workload is being managed by another colleague of ours. Make sure to thank them and appreciate them for stepping up. Doing so also makes it likely that they will be more understanding and more likely to help out when you have to leave early due to any unforeseen issue at home.

I had quite a few dilemmas initially. There were moments when I was dressed to the tee, about to head out to work and Ella would poop in her diaper while I was holding to kiss her goodbye. I would think 'should I stay and change her diaper or should I hand her over to Anna?' Honestly, I have made easier decisions. Because I have such a supportive wife, she would just reach out her hands and tell me to head to work and that she has it handled. Those were moments of relief filled with pangs of guilt, but I used to tell myself 'I am doing as much as I can and I am okay with that.'

There were times when I had a late work meeting and by the time, I would return Ella would be asleep and Anna would be completely exhausted and I would feel like a guilty stranger in our own home. But the harsh reality is that it will be like that, you have to tell yourself you are doing the best you can in your capacity. It may sound like I exist in a utopian world, but maybe I got lucky – but Anna and my workplace were supportive of my entire process which made me realize how important good support systems can be.

Doing justice to your office work while caring for your child

I enjoy my job and what my field of work offers. It does come equipped with its fair share of challenges; however, I do find it to be rewarding. Returning to work after 12 weeks was scary, to say the least. I felt I had forgotten what I had been doing for the past 15 years. There were times at home during my paternity leave where I would get sudden flashes of "what if I forget everything, I know by the time I go to work?" Luckily that did not turn out to be the case.

Since I was working towards setting boundaries in regard to my time, there were also moments where I had to respect the workspace and its rules. It was slightly challenging because I would wonder if I am overstepping a boundary of theirs as well. Organizations and corporations have an established set of rules and regulations that we adhere to, hence while I had my own boundaries to draw in reference to time, they also had their fair share of boundaries which I respected. That is a given in any professional environment.

Moreover, because you have a baby, it is best to be prepared for any unplanned emergencies. Issues such as unanticipated illness or accidents may occur. Hence I would advise that once you return to work, have a list of family members and friends who are comfortable with your child, as well as responsible, in case you cannot make it back in time from work or your employer has an issue with you leaving work. This will enable more flexibility and peace of mind for you because you have a backup in case you are unable to leave office. This list comes in handy during unavoidable absences due to work commitments. Various organizations do offer emergency childcare perks, so you can check with the HR department beforehand.

One of the most important things according to me is communication and honesty. I took my boss into the loop whenever I felt the need. Some would think that they would rather keep their boss out of their domestic issues, but believe me, it really helped when the person who I was answerable to knew my actual situation. Through this, your boss will understand that you respect your workplace and hours as well as recognize that you have urgent issues to tend to at home as well. When there is more space for empathy, I believe it allows for more flexibility. The last thing an employee would want is for their employer to think they are slacking off. Building a narrative of healthy and honest communication helps debunks such notions from the employers' end.

When I returned to work, I felt I gave it my best with whatever was within my capacity. There will always be so much more that you could have done (pesky thoughts that enter your mind every now and then) however, focus on what you are already doing and be okay with that. Once you give yourself that reaffirmation, everything becomes simpler.

Stop overthinking and feeling dad guilt

We talk about mom guilt quite often, but there is dad guilt as well which is usually overlooked. It does exist. The feeling of guilt emerges from feelings of shame and not being able to live up to a standard of parental responsibilities.

It usually happens when I am not 100% present or able to partake in the duties Anna is able to do for Ella such as breastfeeding in the middle of the night and soothing her when she is crying nonstop. However, this guilt is evoked due to society's 'should's of parenting. The truth is that there is no such thing as equal parenting because responsibilities and duties keep shifting, sometimes the mother will be doing more and sometimes the father will be doing more. Moreover, there are some things that fathers cannot do at all, such as the obvious, which is giving birth to the child and breastfeeding. Hence, know that you are doing enough and be okay with that. You cannot do everything, which is why it is emphasized that the mother and father need to share responsibility.

My guilt even comes up when I have to work long hours at the office or have any sort of social outing; a creeping sense of guilt pops up and I feel I am missing out on important moments of Ella growing up. This feeling is hard to quell. I remember Anna calling me on my first day back at work after my paternity leave; she told me Ella was crying a lot because she missed me. At that moment, the pang of guilt and helplessness was a terrible feeling to sit with the entire day.

I was surprised to find that I was not the only one who felt like this. When my group of dad friends and I used to hang out together, they mentioned dad guilt quite often. I drew comfort from the fact that other fathers felt the way I did. Unfortunately, men are conditioned to be more focused on themselves hence switching to a caretaker role once a man becomes a father can lead to unexpected and novel feelings. These feelings usually equate to stress and guilt.

Anna is a certified Pilates instructor and has a studio space where she held classes before we had Ella. Hence, it was easier for Anna to manage her time schedule and work hours (she is her own boss). Thus, when she did resume her Pilate classes, she scheduled classes that were convenient for Ella and her. We summoned the support of our respective mothers and child care. However, leaving Ella alone, without either of us around was scary, to say the least. Before Anna resumed work, I had a reassurance that Anna would be home with Ella but now that Anna was returning to work, I was slightly scared and worried. "Will she be, okay?" "What if she gets hurt and none of us are there?"

– These questions became a common thought process and it was tough to break into it. Initially, it was difficult for Anna and me. We spoke about how we felt and what we could do to lessen our worry. However, we knew our mothers were competent and we were well connected through the phone. While Anna was busy in class, I was more vigilant with my phone.

Moreover, we started to build our trust with the childcare system. We had heard some scary stories, such as the nanny smoking or drinking in the house, not looking after the child, and nannies sleeping on duty; but we had to have faith in the system. There were more good stories than scary stories so we had to have confidence that it would work out for the best. Knowing that we have a backup is reassuring. There were times when our mothers could not babysit Ella; on those days, we would leave Ella with a nanny we hired. We started researching childcare and interviewing nannies earlier on in order to be better acquainted with the nanny and have Ella get comfortable with the nanny as well. Anna and I, along with Ella, took the nanny we finally chose out for lunch, followed by lunch with just Anna and the nanny. We got a sense of what she was like in and out of her work environment. After that, we decided to have the nanny come in two days of the week a couple of weeks before Anna resumed her work. Due to this decision, the nanny and

Ella got the chance to get familiar with each other. We had cameras installed in the house so we would also be able to keep a check on everything through our phones whenever we wanted. Having a system in place gives us the peace of mind we need. Luckily, Ella's nanny is wonderful and she still comes in on days when we need her.

I cannot tell you to stop feeling guilty or overthinking, however, I can guide you and tell you that you are doing the best you can. There will always be ups and downs, it is a part of the journey of parenthood. The fact that you are feeling guilty is a testimony to how much you love your child and how much you want to be there for them.

6

THE FUNDAMENTALS OF A NEW BORN BABY'S EMOTIONAL, MENTAL AND SOCIAL DEVELOPMENT (0-1 YEAR)

I n just a few days after Ella was born, she was so engaged and responsive, constantly following us with her eyes and recognizing our voices. In these early months, parents form trusting bonds with babies by making them feel safe and secure in this world, comforting them, loving them, and meeting their needs.

Even as they grow old, (around six months), they are eager to explore and parents keep it interesting by constantly changing their positions, sometimes on their back and sometimes on their tummy. This lets babies see the world through another perspective which then builds curiosity and helps develop strength and coordination and physical skills needed later for pushing up, sitting up, and crawling. We began to place toys that Ella could grasp out of her reach when she was six months old. This let her experience the thrill of moving her body to reach the goal (grasp the toys). By six months, babies can learn how to communicate – not in words – but back and forth interactions. Parents and caregivers talk and watch to see how babies respond with facial expressions, sounds, and movements. This builds language skills and nurtures social and emotional development in the baby.

By nine months, babies can sit up and freely use both hands to investigate objects; this gives them new ways to explore and build their thinking skills. They are also able to use their fingers to pick up small things such as bits of food. This in turn develops their physical and social-emotional skills as they are able to do more and more for themselves. They even use sounds and actions to communicate, like showing interest in or crawling after a toy they want. When the mother responds by showing how the toy works, it serves as a motivation to keep on communicating. Through this, babies build language, thinking, and social skills.

By 10 months, babies start shaking, banging, filling, and dumping toys. This type of repetition is needed to build thinking skills as problem-solving and learning how things work. Physical skills also grow in this period, babies start crawling and start cruising along with furniture, and taking their first steps. This is the incredible development that takes place in the first year.

I saw it first hand in Ella. She went from rolling to sitting to crawling and walking. Babies progress from learning through observation to using their minds and bodies to discover how things work. Babies move from crying as their primary form of communication to expressing a range of needs and emotions through gestures and sounds.

As babies take their first breath, they also need you for the first time. You and your child develop a strong trusting bond that becomes a blueprint for all future relationships. This is a bond that provides your child with the courage and confidence to explore the larger world. This loving bond with you is what nurtures your child's successive learning; both now and into the future.

You will notice how much your baby evolves and grows in the first year. There are four categories that the baby grows in; social and emotional, cognitive, speech and language, and motor skill development.

Social and emotional development

A large part of the baby's brain is dedicated to understanding, remembering, and reading faces. A big chunk of our behaviour is formed from how we read other people's faces. Make sure you are showing your baby your face and talking to them in a loving and soothing manner. New-born babies do not understand much of what is happening around them – they can feel but not think. Coming out of the womb physically severs the symbiotic relationship between the mother and the child, but it is developed through caring for and tending to the child again. Their only clue to call out for someone is crying, which usually means they are hungry or tired.

Within the first few months, the baby will start to smile. I remember Ella's first smile, luckily Anna and I were around to witness it. It melted my heart. It was the smallest yet most powerful smile in my life. Babies even begin to laugh out loud by the time they turn three months old.

Physical development

You will witness a spurt of growth (you know when they say 'they grow up so fast,' – it is true) in the first few months. An important tip to remember does not to jiggle or shake your baby when they cry during the first three months after they are born. That sort of movement can be scary for them, remember to be gentle with them. Moreover, at this stage, it is easy for babies to be overwhelmed by external stimuli, such as sounds and colours. In terms of hearing, babies have been able to hear while they were in the womb. In reference to sight, because babies have weak eye muscles, they are unable to make sense of visual images. Within the first two months, new-born babies are attracted by bright colours, light, and patterns. Their eyes will begin to move together by the time they turn six weeks. Over the first six months, they will be able to recognize certain faces.

Within the first eight weeks, infants do not have any voluntary control over their bodily movements. They are trying to figure out how to make their bodies move. Pulling, sucking, and grasping is reflexes, however, by eight weeks, babies can lift their heads and begin to kick their legs.

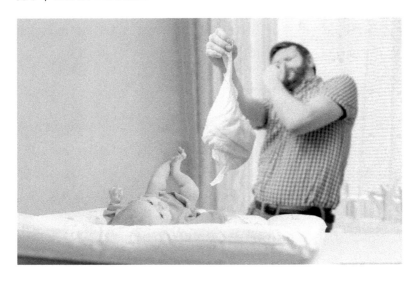

Within the third month, babies start to look at their hands and feet, waving them in the air. Hence, physically, they begin to develop a lot during the first year.

Speech and language

For a new-born baby, crying is the only form of communication to get their needs met. Hence, it is vital to respond and attend to your child's cries during this period so they know that you are there for them when they need you. It provides the child with a sense of security.

Usually, by eight weeks, babies find their voice and begin to make cooing sounds. There is a certain form of communication between you and the baby at this point, you will say something and the baby will make noises in return. It is suggested that you encourage the development of your baby through the following activities;

- Hang a mobile above their cot
- Speak to them in gentle tones and call them by their name frequently
- Make them listen to music
- Sing to them
- Hold, cuddle and rock them
- Mimic their gestures
- When you talk to them, let them look at your face

Cognitive development

Right from the moment they are born, a baby can see. New-born eyes are very sensitive to light hence dimming light will enable the baby to open their eyes more and look at their surroundings. They love to look at their parent's faces, patterns, and colours. New-born babies will focus on faces and objects that are around eight to 12 inches away from their faces. And when a rattle is shaken, they can turn to see where the sound comes from. By the time they turn one year old they develop a lot cognitively. By now they are able to drink from a cup themselves, follow directions and identify images correctly.

Signs to look out for in case of a developmental problem

All children are unique and develop in their own time. There are certain benchmarks to adhere to, however, all babies will not function according to that. Be patient with your child during the process of growing and learning. If you are worried about the development of your child, seek out professional help. There are certain signs to look out for which suggest developmental problems;

- Stiff or limp body (more than usual)
- The baby always has a tight fist
- Not reacting to noise
- Not looking at faces till two months

- Crying for longer than usual periods
- Being extremely quiet
- More than usual difficulties with feeding

It is recommended that you stay vigilant during this time period, in case any developmental problems do arise. If such a situation may arise, make sure to get in touch with a doctor. It is better to identify developmental issues earlier on rather than waiting them out.

In order to summarize what to expect from your newborn baby in the first year refer to the table below;

Birth to three months

- Smiling and following people with their eyes
- Inclined to look at brighter colors
- Gurgle
- Explore their hands and feet
- Able to lift their head while lying on their stomach
- Cry frequently, but feel better when they are held

Four to six months

- Can laugh on top of smiling and able to imitate sounds they hear

- Can understand that their legs and feet are a part of their body
- Are able to sit up
- Can rollover
- Are able to grasp things and begin to put things in their mouth

Seven months to a year

- Start to believe they are big and start to take the first steps
- Begin to dance and move to tunes they like
- Play simple games such as peek-a-boo
- Can identify when their name is said out
- Begin to vocalize
- Start to discover, shake, and hit objects together
- Able to look for and find objects hidden out of their sight
- Develop the ability to sit up by themselves
- Build enough strength to pull themselves up to stand and try to walk

Parenting styles and their impact on your child

What exactly is parenting style? It is the standard practice and strategy that parents use in their child-rearing. The idea of parenting styles was introduced in the 1960s by Diana Baumrind. She draws relationships between parenting styles and basic behaviour in children.

You may not know it, but you must be following a certain style of parenting. It is good to be aware of the style you adopt because it does have an impact on your child's outcome as well as your relationship with your child. More importantly, raise yourself before you raise your child; in simpler terms, this means that be more aware of who you are, how you function, and being in tune with your emotions. There are four types of parenting styles and they are divided and vary between two dimensions; warmth and control. The first key dimension is warmth; how much affection and how much love you show to your child. The second key dimension is control; how much structure you impose upon the child and how involved you are in the child's life, such as setting a bedtime routine, helping with school, and knowing feeding times. Within warmth and control, there are levels of high and low warmth and high and low control, which give birth to the four styles of parenting; authoritative, authoritarian, permissive, and uninvolved. You may find yourself wondering which style of parenting you are practicing and which style is best for your child's long-term outcome.

I for one drifted towards working on being an authoritative parent with Ella as did Anna. Of course, it is not a constant smooth ride, we would both have our days of switching between parenting styles, and however, we mostly adhered to being authoritative. When we found out Anna was pregnant, we did get caught up in the preparations and readying the house and so on. However, there were a lot of times when I used to sit down with myself and think 'what kind of parent will I be to Ella?' I used to wonder, 'Will I be strict with her?' 'Will I be a cool dad and allow more candy and screen time?' 'Will I let her do everything my parents never allowed me to?' I did not know till I had Ella. I gravitate more towards authoritative, as I mentioned before, but I am guilty of being permissive a lot of times as well. There are moments where I have been an authoritarian parent with Ella also, but seldom. My go-to style is definitely authoritative and believes me, I was not born an authoritative parent, it took me a while to practice it and be mindful of how I am behaving towards Ella. While we are told to be patient and loving with our children, remember to show the same patience and love to yourself as well.

Authoritative parenting (Just right)

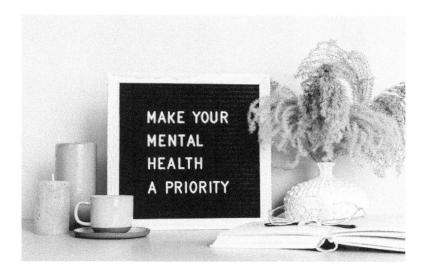

The authoritative style is high warmth and high control. Authoritative parents are very loving, affectionate and also offer a sense of structure in the child's life. This type of parent gives reasonable demands and sets consistent limits, they express warmth and affection and listen to the child's point of view. It is more of a give and takes relationship, akin to democracy. Within this style, the parent is still the parent but also expresses warmth. For instance, if the child wants to stay up past their bedtime, instead of saying no, the parents suggest talking about it and ask 'why do you think you should stay up? The parent also conveys their concerns to the child, such as 'I do not want you to be tired tomorrow,' and the parent and child come to a compromise.

Such parents usually set rules and encourage the child to follow these rules for their betterment. Authoritative parents do not use power to gain anything from the child.

Such parents offer guidance in a rationalized manner which leads to effective communication between the child and the parent. Authoritative parenting is the best style of parenting because it leads to children being emotionally healthy. Children who grow up with authoritative parents are self-assured, great in school, have great social skills, are less involved in alcohol, have good self-esteem, and better-coping strategies.

Authoritarian parenting (Too hard)

Do not confuse authoritarian with authoritative. They are completely different styles of parenting. This is a combination of high control and low warmth. Authoritarianism is more about conformity and obedience and sticks to the orthodox narrative of 'I am the adult and you are the child.' There is no discussion and it is a very strict relationship. Such parents are also called helicopter parents. Authoritarian parents wish to shape the behavior and personality of their child according to a certain standard, and if these standards are not met, they are punished. Usually, there is no logic or rationale behind these set standards the parents wish their children to adhere to. Such parents have high demands from their children, are less engaged, do not encourage open communication, and expect their children to be extremely obedient. If the aforementioned scenario of the child asking for an extension in their bedtime is adapted to this style of parenting, the parent would say 'no' without any hesitation and there would be no room for negotiation.

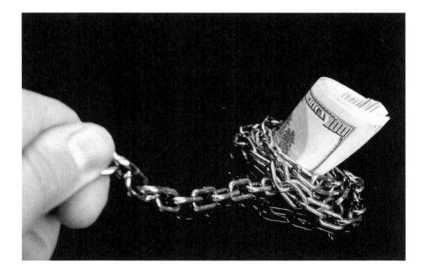

Children who have authoritarian parents usually turn out to be anxious, withdrawn, and unhappy. They generally have lower self-confidence and poor coping mechanisms. They also lack self-discipline, are associated with poor academic behaviour, have unprotected sex, and suffer from substance abuse. Moreover, such children are more dependent on parental guidance since they lack self-confidence.

However, in some cultures, such as Southeast Asian families, such styles of parenting are usually equated to authoritative parenting and it is believed that children of these parents turn out to be as mentally healthy as children of authoritative parents.

Permissive parenting (Too soft)

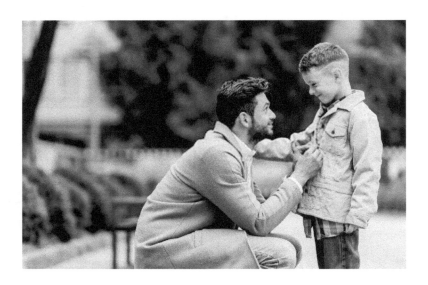

Permissive parenting is characterized by high warmth and low control polar opposite of authoritative. In permissive parenting, children run the show and anything goes. The parent makes few demands and rarely uses punishment. They try to play the role of a friend rather than a parent. It is not bad to try to be a friend, but there are limits to that as well. Such parents tend to behave in a very affirmative manner and avoid conflict. Furthermore, permissive parents escape any sort of behavioural control, shirk away from establishing rules, and have fewer expectations from their children. Such parents give the space to their children to partake in activities without thinking about repercussions. This style of parenting has an increased level of responsiveness.

You may have heard the term 'indulgent parent,' it actually means permissive parent. Because such parents demand next to nothing from their children are more indulgent, the children turn out lacking self-discipline. Moreover, the children of permissive parents are generally unhappy and lack the skill of self-regulation. They also do not do well in school and do not respond well to authority.

Uninvolved parents

Uninvolved parents have low warmth and low control. They are, as the title suggests, uninvolved and indifferent to the child's needs, especially emotional needs. They even tend to be neglectful at times. This type of parenting is basically about filling the child's basic needs such as being fed, drinking water, and providing shelter. This is also termed as rejecting and neglecting to parent. Such parents usually struggle with substance abuse or are overly involved in careers with no time for their child or family.

There are very low levels of involvement and these types of parents are generally stricter as well. They do not have demands, neither do they have any responsiveness within them, and do not show any intimacy towards their child.

Uninvolved parenting leads to emotionally withdrawn, fearful, and anxious individuals. Such children are also more at risk of substance abuse. They have low self-esteem and low self-confidence. They do not fare well in school.

While parenting styles do play an important role in the outcome of a child, it is important to know that other factors are at play in a child's development as well. Factors such as the child's temperament, societal influences, and culture also make up a big chunk of how your child can turn out when they reach adulthood.

The concept of parenting has evolved over the years. Now, parents are much more involved and more active in their children's lives. We want to give the best to our children, we want them to be the best and we want the world to think they are the best. But hey, slow down. The best according to who? Society has millions of standards and it is not humanly possible to adhere to all of them. Hence, what do you think is best for your child? Give them space and intellectual freedom to explore. Let them develop an innate sense of wonder, give them the freedom to think and discover. Encourage reading, playing, adventure, and outdoor activities. Stimulate their emotional side and encourage them to be in touch with their feelings.

In today's day and age, being worried about every single thing about your child or what your child is doing equates to responsible parenting. Parents generally hover over their children to make sure they are doing everything right because it somehow reflects on them as well. It is important to know that your child is his own person, as are you. Most parents tend to over-look emotions in the chase to be the perfect parent and raise the perfect child. Perfection is subjective, hence do the best you can and raise your child to be a kind-hearted and tolerant human because the world needs more people like that. As Frank Pittman once said, "Fathering is not something perfect men do, but some-thing that perfects the man."

7

WORKING ON MY PARENT-CHILD RELATIONSHIP

So when parents I knew used to say 'I always put my child before myself,' I would find it hard to believe; there had to be a balance right? Turns out I was wrong! It is all about the child for the first few months and maybe a year also. However, I am not complaining, rather stating the real facts about parenthood. Moreover, it was not just about keeping Ella healthy and functioning, it was also about me building an emotional bond with my child.

Focusing on the needs of my child

Within the first few months, all Ella required was naps, sleep, milk, and diaper changes. While it sounds easy, in reality, it is a non-stop process. Initially, your baby has to be fed every two to three hours, which amounts to eight to 12 times a day. When the child is around three weeks old, you may practice putting off feeding for a short time by engaging in other activities such as rocking or talking to your baby. As the baby grows with each passing day, their nervous system becomes mature enough to handle the slight delay between feeding times. During night-time feeding, Anna had told me that I should not play or talk to the baby, keep the lights dim and use a soft and gentle voice. By the time they turn two months old, babies automatically eat less at night and by the time they hit their four-month mark, they begin to get distracted by sights and sounds and delay their feeding time.

I noticed this change in Ella personally. When it used to be my turn to feed her when she was around five months old, it would be more difficult because she is more easily distracted, but during this time, it was also easier to socialize with her during meal times. By the time they hit the six-month mark, most babies do begin to eat solid foods. However, before you make the decision of feeding your baby solids, consult your doctor.

The next need you will be spending a lot of time catering to will be changing diapers. I was surprised at the number of diapers Anna and I would change in a day. You do not have a choice because you cannot let urine or poop sit in the diaper for too long – it causes skin irritation. You may have to change at least three to six in a day.

And then comes another important need; sleep. To be honest, I love and need to sleep a lot at this age as well. When Ella was a new-born, she used to sleep for around 17 to 18 hours a day, but not on a go. She usually used to wake up after every two to three hours. They need to wake up because they have to be fed. It will remain like this for the first few weeks. There are a few things to note in a baby's sleep cycle. There are murmuring periods for around every hour while the baby sleeps and this is known as active sleep. Other than that the sleep cycle consists of drowsy sleep, deep sleep, and active sleep. During drowsy sleep, babies can be awakened easily. During deep sleep is not awakened easily and during active sleep, the baby is restless and has rapid breathing.

During the first couple of months, I noticed that Ella would sleep through loud noises as compared to when she was around four months old. During this period, it is important to establish a bedtime routine for your baby because during this age period they sleep for at least seven to eight hours. I used to sing and rock Ella to sleep in a dim room, which would help her fall asleep faster. As Ella grew up, it would be more difficult to put her to sleep because of all the adrenaline and excitement they feel throughout the day. Hence, I strongly suggest you set a routine when they are three months old and build it up.

Another need of a new-born baby is naps. Naps become common as they grow older. When I used to run errands with Ella, it would be tempting to make her nap so I could go about doing my thing easily. As lovely as it sounds, it is not practical because you do not want your child to be constantly napping, it destabilizes their set schedule. When your baby turns six months old, make them take longer naps during the day and increase the time between each nap time – it leads to better sleep at night. Make sure you establish a set routine for nap times and adhere to it as much as possible.

The importance of building an emotional tie with your child

As I mentioned earlier, it is necessary to be there to fulfil the needs of your child, but it is also important to focus on building an emotional bond with your child. Since I had taken paternity leave, I think I was able to bond with Ella quite a bit during the first three months.

A baby's brain has a lot of growing to do, and you can help it develop through bonding with them – lots of smiles, cuddles, and loving words. For some fathers, bonding happens right away and for others, it may take some time. Know it is never too late to bond with your child. Physical affections make babies grow, try cuddling your baby close towards the left side of your chest so they can hear your heartbeat. Your baby may find it reassuring Moreover, skin-on-skin contact such as a baby massage can make your baby feel secure as well.

Eye contact is especially good for bonding development. When your baby deliberately catches your eyes, you can look right back in their eyes and maintain eye contact till they look away. Furthermore, babies love to hear you talk, so give a running commentary as you go through the day, talk about what you are doing and name the things and objects around you. Babies also love sing-song voices and funny noises. Using facial expressions when you talk helps your baby learn the connection between words and feelings. When your baby starts to babble you can repeat the sounds they make and practice taking turns at making conversation. During the time I used to spend with Ella, I would be speaking to her as if she was an adult. I would tell her about my day, my work, and my general feelings. In return, she would smile and make babbling noises. It is one of the most adorable communications. I actually used to look forward to coming home from work and just holding her in my arms and speaking to her. It was my time with her and it helped build a bond between her and me.

It is never too early to start reading to your baby. Babies love looking at the pictures in books, listening to your voice, and spending time with you. Singing songs is a fun way to develop your baby's language skills. Try it in the car, in the bath, at bedtime, even if you are off-key. Your baby will love the rhythm and will be soothed by your voice. I do not have the loveliest of voices, but I found a rapt audience in Ella. She was one person who would love smiling, bobbing up and down, and gurgling whenever I would sing to her. Smile at your baby, when they see you smile they release chemicals in their body that help them grow and make them feel good. And who does not love a baby smiling? It is the most pleasing feeling.

Play simple games with them such as peek-a-boo and pat a cake. This can help with their learning and movement skills. If you find that your baby's gaze is averted, that means they may not want to play anymore or might begin to get tired. If that is the case, try a change of activity, put them on the floor to gaze around, or put them to bed for a nap.

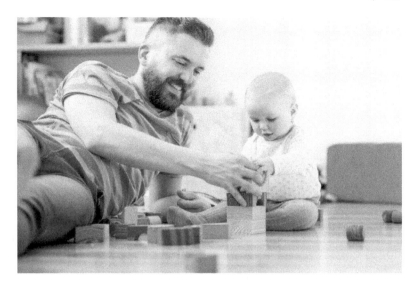

It does not take much for a father to bond with his baby. It is the small things you can do; they go a long way. Other than the fact that it is a beautiful bond, there are also benefits to fathers bonding emotionally with their children. Due to father's spending time with their child, the child's mental and physical development is enhanced as opposed to children whose fathers do not take an active role in their upbringing. Moreover, fathers feel less stressed and more confident when they build on a bond with their children. I can vouch for that. Spending time with Ella, be it speaking to her, holding her, playing with her, always made me feel less anxious or stressed, especially if I had a long and gruelling day. Furthermore, research highlights that solid father and child bonds deter issues like depression, crime, and drug abuse in the future. Such children also fare better at school, have successful relationships with loved ones. What's more, is that grown male adults who had a healthy relationship with their fathers during their childhood were better able to handle stress and anxiety.

Hence, it is imperative that fathers spend valuable time with their children and help them become healthy functioning adults. Most fathers are guilty of getting caught up in their jobs and building their careers, after all, their justification is that they are doing it for their children. However, it is equally important that you provide for them emotionally as well, not just financially. They also justify not being wholly present by thinking the mother is already with the child, that should be enough, but I am sorry to say that it is not enough. You share an individual and special relation with your child as does your partner. Over the years, your relationship with your child will evolve differently in comparison to your partner's relationship with your child. You cannot expect the mother's presence to be enough and neither can the mother expect the father's presence to be enough in the child's life. Taking out time in the day for your child and family needs to be a priority – a priority that should not be overlooked.

Understanding the type of attachment, you have with your child

The types of attachment styles were first categorized by Mary Ainsworth in the '70s, her work is inspired by John Bowlby's (the inventor of attachment theory) work, which came about in the '50s. Attachments are a continuous process of pursuing and upholding a level of proximity with another individual. Expectations that people have from relationships with others, built on the relationship with their primary caregiver as infants are known as attachment styles. Attachment styles play an essential role in the healthiness of our relationships, relationships with partners, the workplace, and with friends. The attachment theory argues that a strong emotional and physical bond to one primary caregiver in our first years of life is critical to our development – it sets the template for building relationships with people. Over time, we use this same template in all our relationships. If our bonding is strong and we are securely attached, then we feel safe to explore the world. We know there is always that safe base to which we can return at any time. However, if our bond is weak, we feel insecurely attached. We are afraid to leave or explore a rather scary-looking world because we are afraid that we cannot return. After having read about attachment styles, I automatically began to think about my attachment style with my mother and father as well.

Moreover, it also made me more mindful of the type of attachment style I want Ella to create with me. Sometimes we do not realize how much attachment styles influence us.

There are four types of attachment styles that your child can develop with you. They are as follows;

- **Secure** (Flexible, treat each relationship as it is, effective at problem-solving)
- **Anxious – Ambivalent** (Clingy, a lot of unaddressed needs)
- **Anxious – Avoidant** (Much more independent, tell themselves they do not need a relationship, tend to escape situations where people want to express strong emotions because it makes them anxious)
- **Fearful** – Avoidant (Combination of the above two; conscious need to have a deep relationship, but very afraid of abandonment and their behaviours are erratic)

Knowing about attachment styles and beforehand enables you to be more mindful of the attachment style you want to establish between yourself and your child. Most times, when people are unaware of their own attachment style, they will parent their child in the same way they were parented by their parents.

Secure

Children who have a secure attachment with their primary caregiver get distressed when their caregivers are not around and become happy when they are around. When secure children are scared, they turn to their parents to seek comfort. Any contact – physical or emotional – is accepted wholly by securely attached children. Moreover, such children prefer parents over strangers.

How do parents of securely attached children behave? Well, they take out more time to play with their children, are quick at responding to their needs, and more responsive to their children in comparison to the other attachment styles. Moreover, there are five primary conditions needed to cultivate a secure attachment style with your child.

- **Felt safety:** The child must feel safe. This establishes trust. Safety and protection do not just mean locking in a car seat or the crib is secure. Rather, it means soothing a child after the child hears a loud noise and gets frightened. This helps the child internalize that someone is there for them and can help them – hence the world is safe for them. As a parent, you may think that you have a tall order of immediate needs to respond to at all times; however, the motto to follow here is 'more often than not.'
- **Feeling seen and known:** The apparent behaviour is atonement to understand the inner state of what your child's internal world is like. This is important because the child has one cry, and it is up to the parent to decipher whether it is a hungry cry, pain cry, or asleep cry. It is a personal intuition when you feel your child is behaving in an offhanded manner. This in-turn helps the child with their self-development because they know they have something and someone is out there trying to help them figure out what it is.
- **Felt comfort:** The child needs to internalize

these feelings. It is not just about picking the child up when they cry while looking at your phone, it is also important to be mindful and present with your child while soothing them so the child receives the internal message that when they are upset, they will be comforted, it is not the end of the world and their need is being met – remember to tell yourself 'More often than not.' They will be taught through parental behaviours how to have emotional regulation which they will be able to do themselves as they grow up. Through this, they will learn to internalize self-soothing.

- **Feeling valued:** The only way to create self-esteem in a child is that the child has a sense of accomplishment and that the parent or caregiver rejoices in that sense of accomplishment, this is called amplifying the effect. The child then feels really good about themselves, and that is how self-esteem is created. Since children learn through their eyes and not their ears, what you can do is show appreciation and acknowledgment through body language, expressions, and verbally. Since most of this is felt before actual words develop, words do not mean as much as a loving look or an adoring look. They assess

everything in the world through how you
present it to them.

- **Felt support:** This feeling comes a bit after
  infancy. When the child is encouraged to be
  who they are and are motivated to explore their
  own interests while they have your support,
  they feel they can go off in the world and find
  their own path because they believe there are
  people in the world who want the best for
  them.

You know you have a secure attachment style with your
parent or child if you have confidence in your partner
and relationship. Feelings such as trust, comfort,
connection, space to grow, healthy independence from
each other, and communicating loving feelings are
common in such an attachment. Such individuals are
able to provide support to their partners as well as
reach out for help when they need it. Furthermore,
securely attached children tend to become more
empathic and mature adults in the future.

In a study, researchers discovered that women who had
a secure attachment style harboured increased positive
feelings with their romantic adult relationships as
opposed to women who had an insecure attachment
style.

Anxious – Ambivalent

Children who form the anxious ambivalent attachment style have parents who were inconsistent with their caregiving and meeting the child's emotional needs in a stable and consistent manner. Most times, parents may act like this on an unconscious level. For instance, if a parent hears their child crying for warmth or affection, the parent fulfills their need sometimes and sometimes does not fulfil the need and lets the child resort to self-soothing. Hence, the caregiver comes off as unpre-dictable to the child. This gives rise to the feeling of internal conflict within the child – they are happy when the parent is attentive and confused and sad when the parents are not attentive; hence the term ambivalent attachment. On one hand, they doubt the caregiver and on the other, they also yearn for the care-giver's attention to meet their emotional needs, so they end up clinging to them. This lays the foundation for the child's ambivalent behavior pattern. It usually pans out as indecisiveness and uncertainty.

As an adult, this usually comes out in a lot of indecision in making even the simplest of decisions. What to eat, what to wear, where to go on holiday. Moreover, deciding becomes more difficult when an individual feels conflicted, hence the feeling of ambivalence.

Moreover, they become clingy romantic partners and feel insecure about exploring the world around them.

In an experiment conducted by Ainsworth, she observed how after time apart from their mothers, a few children were confused, restless, and evaded eye contact with their mothers upon reuniting with them. However, at the same time, the children were observed to be extremely clingy with their mothers upon reuniting with them. While the child was channelling all its energy towards staying next to and around the mother, it seemed that the child was unable to derive any comfort from her presence.

While the parent or caregiver is away from an anxious ambivalent child, they will become visibly upset and angry, however, while they resist being soothed upon being reunited with the parent, they cling to the parent regardless, because they are seeking safety from them. Anxious ambivalent babies have very high emotional needs and feel they cannot go on without support from others, and yet they are ambivalent because when they turn to others for help, they are turned down or hurt in return, hence they are stuck in a loop. Some of these babies are very difficult to soothe.

Being an anxious ambivalent child can affect how the child socializes, the way they comprehend and perform tasks. Since they are so caught up in trying to attain the attention of their parents or caregiver, they are not able to absorb any information or instructions. Most times, in a school setting, the 'class clown' stereotype is an anxious ambivalent child. Such behaviours in a school setting can often lead to a misdiagnosis of attention deficit hyperactivity disorder (ADHD) when in actuality they feel extreme anxiety in their internal world. The sense of self in an anxious ambivalent child is very shaky because deep down they feel unlovable and unwanted. However, at the same time sometimes people have been there for them, so maybe they are lovable? There is a lot of confusion. And maybe the best way to characterize the sense of self within such children is what other people think of them.

In a school setting, there can be a mixed presentation of how severe attachment issues are and whether or not relationships have been hurtful in the past. On the lighter side, you can see a child who likes to be the center of attention and is preoccupied with what people think instead of focusing on their school work. On the desperate side, such children tend to get into intense and bad relationships, get mad when relationships fail and look for signs of abandonment and failure even when there are not any. They never feel satisfied in relationships. They always know something is wrong and feel there is something to be worried about, which is not a healthy mind space to be in.

Anxious avoidant

This type of attachment style usually develops within the first 18 months of a child's life. Usually, parents of an anxious, avoidant child are not present and around so much in a child's life and ignore the child's needs by responding in a manner that is rejecting the child. Moreover, any emotions and feelings shown from such children are usually frowned upon or dismissed from the parent or caregiver because the parent may want to avoid emotions as well.

This style of parenting pushes children towards forming a premature sense of independence. Since such children's needs are not being met – intentionally or unintentionally – as they grow older they begin to look after their own needs and begin to self-soothe and create a false sense of independence. Due to this, they feel they do not need anyone to support them and can take care of themselves.

An anxious-avoidant parent or caregiver may move away physically from their child when the child shows fear or sadness, they even shame their child for showing emotion and feelings. Moreover, such parents and caregivers want their children to become independent which may not be possible for their age. Phrases such as 'grow up,' 'do not cry,' or 'you are behaving like a baby,' are used when their children show any signs of emotion. Hence, the child feels it is pointless to cry out for attention from the caregiver or parent and suppress their internal need and desire for love and showing any sort of emotion because it will end up getting rejected and put aside. Because emotions are shunned by the caregiver or parent, the child stops showing them. Through this suppression, they can still be close to the caregiver or parent. Growing up in such an emotionless environment can lead to a strong sense of rejection within the child and their attachment system shuts down, hence creating a vast disconnect from their needs.

In the aforementioned experiment conducted by Ainsworth, anxious-avoidant children evaded contact with their mother once reunited with them. Even though they put up an external façade of not needing their mother, they acted just as anxious and distraught as securely attached children when separated from the mother, except they made an effort not to show it. Avoidant children want to stay close to their caregiver, but without actually having to interact with them.

Children who develop an anxious-avoidant style of attachment are usually precocious, seem very self-contained and seldom show signs of needing any sort of love or warmth. Over time they eventually forget they have feelings; they have very little awareness of emotions. Does that not sound unhealthy? However, they do have good self-regulatory abilities. They like to take care of themselves and enjoy exploring the world because it distracts them from relationship anxieties.

While such children may like to socialize, they might have a problem connecting with people and feel they should not depend on others for anything. They may look calm, but deep down they feel a lot of anxiety.

As adults, they become external-focused and accomplishment and achievement-focused. In relationships they usually shirk away from emotions and intense situations, they withdraw because they feel overwhelmed and disconnected from the situation.

Fearful Avoidant

This style of attachment is also known as disorganized. This is the worst type of attachment style a child can form. Children who suffer from abuse and trauma usually form this attachment style. Such children's parents or caregivers behave chaotically and the children see them as scary because of their aggressive behavior. They do not feel safe in this world either.

Usually, such parents exhibit unpredictable and erratic behaviors in their parenting method. They may be extremely loving on some days and may not meet the child's basic needs on other days, which in turn gives birth to a sense of fear for their safety in the child.

Being exposed to trauma and emotional abuse has the ability to cause long-term harmful effects on the child, which alters the emotional regulation of the child's brain. Unconsciously, the child figures out that the caregiver or parent is unable to meet their needs. Then again, the parent's behavior may not always be intentional. Such parents may have also had a disordered type of childhood. Since most parents parent in the same way they were parented, their actions may be unintentional. Parents of fearfully avoidant children have not worked through their own trauma, hence allowing the trauma to internalize and affecting their behavior over time. Hence, they can get easily triggered by a child's cry and also dissociate from their child.

Caregivers or parents of fearful-avoidant children may have low confidence in raising a child, hence they get scared and are overwhelmed by the entire process. Due to this, the child seems terrifying to them which prompts the caregiver to behave unpredictably. While they might reward a certain behavior of the child, they may also punish the child for the same behavior on another day. This will obviously leave the child scared and confused. The most important person in the child's life – the primary caregiver – from whom they desire warmth, love, and connection, becomes a source of fear for them.

Hence, due to the unpredictability of the caregiver's actions, fearful-avoidant children cannot figure out how to have their needs met – they are left clutching on to nothing, feeling confused. Imagine being a child and experiencing such feelings. It is alarming, to say the least.

In the aforementioned study by Ainsworth, fearful-avoidant children were observed to behave in a conflicting manner towards their mothers. They were noted as running towards the caregiver, but then changing course midway and running away. They would also act out against their mother. Since the child yearns for comfort from the mother, they automatically want to be near them and with them, but in a fearful-avoidant child, being near the mother also triggers a sense of warning and fear.

Such children usually stare at their caregiver or parent but tend to avoid eye contact, they shout and wail nonstop to grab the attention of the caregiver, and display conflicting emotions, such as, needing attention and then shirking away from it right after getting it.

Older fearful-avoidant children find it difficult to self-soothe and find it hard to open up to other people. Due to them feeling unsafe and not secure in the world, they seem to be searching for the next negative occasion. Moreover, such children do not know much about personal boundaries. They tend to talk about inappropriate issues with strangers. They seem to act the same way towards people they know and strangers, have no sense of guilt, have difficulty concentrating and maintaining friendships and romantic relationships in their adult life. As adults, they may dissociate, just as their caregiver did, have low self-esteem, have trust issues, seek constant approval, and tend to gravitate towards abusive relationships.

THE FIRST TIME FATHER 2-IN 1 VALUE BUNDLE | 393

Such children will need therapy since the behaviors they resort to can be damaging.

A newfound connection with my father

I do think it is justified to say that my relationship with my father was extremely strained or broken. I thought I had a completely normal relationship with my father up until I began therapy and became a father myself. My father never hurt me intentionally, it was just unfortunate that he was not around as much when we were growing up.

I was around nine years old and I had received an award at school. I remember holding the award extremely carefully all the way home from school. My mom hugged me and congratulated me and even gave me a Popsicle as a reward. When my father came home, I ran to him excitedly to show him the award as well, however, all he did was smile and pat me on my head and went back to whatever he was doing. I think my mom noticed the look of dejection on my face

As I had mentioned earlier, my mother was our primary caregiver and because parenting was way different in their generation, my father not helping out and being around was not a big deal. He would be with us on weekends, would watch TV with us, and read to us. I know he wanted me to be an engineer or a doctor, careers which I did not aspire towards. Growing up, he would sit me down and talk to me about medicine, how trains worked and how planes flew. Now that I look back, I think that was his way of showing his interest in my life. When I opted to take accounting as a major, he was upset with me, but luckily he was able to see I enjoyed it and supported me. He is a man of few words, has a very strong sense of wrong and right, and does not express himself too much, hence I never confided much in him. Even as adults, our conversations mostly centred on sports, the weather, and politics – the clichés. Beyond that, I found it difficult to have a conversation with my father. It did not make me love him less, I feel I never really connected with him how I would have liked to.

I know I did not want to be that type of father to Ella and so I feel I behave in the opposite manner. I am emotionally and physically present for Ella, play with her, support her, help her explore, tell her how much I love her and appreciate her for the smallest of things. Maybe this is me making up for what I did not receive as a child from my father – filling in the gaping wound my father left me with – a wound that called out for love and attention.

However, becoming a father, something shifted within me. I somehow discovered a newfound love for my father as well. Yes, I was aware that my father had wounded me as a child – abandonment and neglect wounds to be more specific – nevertheless, I worked through it with my therapist and came to the point where I was able to forgive him for doing that. Moreover, I took out time to speak to my father (after we had Ella) and tell him how much I had expected from him as a child and how he was unable to meet those expectations of mine. It was a sad conversation, to say the least. I felt I had hurt him by telling him how I felt, seeing him sitting across me, slightly hunched with greying hair, broke my heart, but I needed to tell him.

In turn, he told me that he tried to be the best father he could and he was sorry for not being able to do more for me. Having heard that from him somehow made me feel lighter – it was an apology I did not know I was looking for. Moreover, it made me realize he was human, he made mistakes and I also allowed myself to look at things through his perspective. Having this conversation worked in the favor of our relationship. See, you do not just become a father by giving birth to a child, it takes effort to build a relationship. I find myself being able to talk more easily to my father now, sometimes we go for a walk with Ella, and we have found a new hobby – Tamiya plastic model kits. He has started to keep more in touch via texting and calling and I cannot begin to tell you how much I appreciate that. I suppose it is his way of trying to make up for lost time with me. And it is not just me, he is working on becoming more vocal with my other siblings, as well as my mom. It is heart-warming, to say the least. What's more, is that his relationship with Ella has benefited a lot, he is more loving and affectionate towards her than he was with us. Being a father is not easy, hence when I became one, it made me empathize with my father which helped us improve our relationship.

8

EFFECTIVE PARENTING

After Mirabelle gave birth to Ella, time had no meaning for us. Yes we were a family now and Ella was the most beautiful addition in our lives, but taking out time for ourselves became increasingly difficult. Regaining a sense of self after having a child is hard to do because you are lost in your day-to-day care. Take out time to find yourself again. I was a bag of emotions in the first few months. You may be feeling a myriad of emotions; happiness, sadness, gratitude, or surprise – whatever emotions you are feeling, allow yourself to feel them because it is okay.

Self-care and managing my emotions

While you may find yourself sitting and staring into space, at the back of your head you will be aware of your baby's whereabouts, what they are up to, and if they are safe or not – that can be mentally tiring as well. You will always find yourself occupied or preoccupied. Being busy and always being on your toes is somehow seen as a positive aspect nowadays. Well, it is not.

Take a deep breath and step back. If you and your partner burn out, you will not be able to be there for your child. Simply put, it is mentally and physically exhausting and draining. Your emotions are all over the place, you are juggling between your family, your newborn baby, your job, and the house. Where do you fit in? Being the best father to our child and practicing effective parenting requires us to be the best version of ourselves and in order to do that, we need to make intentional choices and changes in our life to look after ourselves. Fortunately, as Millennial parents, the idea of self-care is extremely important.

Following are some tips to be an effective parent and taking care of your needs;

- Dedicate time to yourself: Make self-care a priority. Even taking a few minutes for yourself on a daily basis will help you face the day with a clearer mind.
- Turn self-care into a habit: It needs to be

something that everyone in the family knows is happening for you. Once your family knows your boundaries, they will respect it as well and it becomes normalized.

- Establish some realistic expectations from yourself: The best way to do this is to think about optional versus necessary, for instance, your daily share in the household chores can be optional, but keeping the house safe for your child is necessary.
- Make to-do lists: It becomes easier to see what you have to do as opposed to what you need to do. Plus, it makes it easier to keep a tab on all your commitments in the day.
- Ask for help: Mirabelle and I hired house help, which was a blessing, we had our family and friends and that really allowed us time for ourselves. If you have the option, reach out for help or hire help if your finances allow you to.
- Take out much-needed me-time: What do you define as me-time? Is it going to the gym, going for a walk, sipping on coffee and doing nothing, watching your favorite show, scrolling through your Twitter or Instagram feed, reading? Whatever it may be, make sure to carve out that space for yourself because it helps you feel re-energized and more fulfilled.

400 | ALFIE THOMAS

- Make plans with other people: You are much less likely to give up on an appointment if someone else is involved. It could even be a 30-minute coffee plan or a jog in the park with a friend.
- Keep a journal: If you feel overwhelmed with emotions, try keeping a journal and writing down what you are feeling. Penning your thoughts down relieves stress and allows for introspection.
- Exercise: Make sure you get in some form of physical exercise every day, even if it is for 20 minutes. Exercising improves your mood as well as your mental health.
- Take a break from electronics: In the 21st century, not being glued to your phone is akin to blasphemy. However, always being on your phone is not healthy. Sometimes it is good to disconnect from electronic devices.

Remember, taking out time for yourself does not make you a bad father! Believe me when I say it works wonders when you make time for yourself. Start off small and build a routine if that helps. Mirabelle and I spoke about our own self-care and self-time, we knew when the other had their personal time and would respect that. Moreover, I always felt more re-energized and in a better mood after I took time to do my own thing, which was going to the gym and watching a show on Netflix. When Mirabelle would go for a spa day or a walk in the park, I would look after Ella and vice versa. I believe it helped Mirabelle and I maintain a healthy relationship with ourselves as well as with Ella.

9

ADVICE FOR NEW DADS

B eing a dad is not easy and that little bundle of joy can bring new dynamics to your relationship. Following are a few concerns most new fathers have and I will tell you how to work through them.

How to keep your relationship healthy

- Listen to your partner: Instead of trying to solve your partner's problems, just hear her out. Men have a tendency to go into a problem-solving mode instead of listening at times. Ask her what she needs from and be more empathic.
- Do not complain a lot: Your partner carried the baby and gave birth, so while you may be dealing with mood swings and being low, it is nothing compared to what she had to go

through. Hence, be mindful of complaining to her.

- Offer help unsolicited: Do not ask if she needs help, instead make a statement to help. If she usually cooks, tell her "Hey I will make dinner tomorrow" instead of "Do you want me to make dinner tomorrow?"
- Plan time away from the child: If you can do a weekend, or an overnight stay, or even dinner for a couple of hours, do it.
- Give her compliments: Something non-physical or non-sexual preferably. Tell her what a great mom she is or how you appreciate her.
- Say I love you more: Send a text or leave a note whenever you can but do not make it sexual. Just be loving and nice.

Do not take things personally

Your baby is not out to get you, it may feel like that sometimes but your baby is just making sense of the world around them. Your baby will cry and whine and this may stress you out initially. If your baby cries when you hold them, just hold them more often, if they cry when you bathe them, do it more often. Babies thrive on familiarity, so things being done repeatedly create comfort between you and the baby.

Focus on quality of time, not quantity of time

If you have a lot of time available or are the primary caretaker that is great. However, for many new dads, we may feel guilty for not spending enough time with our baby. We feel the more time we spend, the better it is. But spending a lot of time also conflicts with our work schedule or other commitments. What is quality time? It is being present at the moment, giving affection, playing, or feeding – it being specifically focused on your child and not distracted by your phone or having a conversation with someone else. Spend one on one time with the baby as well. There is something special when you spend time alone with your baby. It becomes fun and you become confident in your ability as a dad. It allows you to connect, talk and play with your child.

Be okay with your mistakes

We all make mistakes as first-time fathers, accept them, learn from them and move on. It does not mean that you are not capable of taking care of your child, it just means you lack experience. You may have not changed the diaper properly or miscalculated their nap time, and that is okay.

Enjoy the present

When you are a new dad you will often think about the future; 'I cannot wait till she walks or talks. You do not want such thoughts to overshadow the current stage your child is in; just enjoy that stage for the time being. You will not get that time back because time goes by fast. Before you know it, your child has grown, hence the time to do it is now. Being a dad is not about trying to handle every 'what if' that could come along as much as it is about being in the moment.

Be confident in yourself

We get overwhelmed, nervous, and stressed and that is okay but you have to have confidence that you will be able to do this. It might feel like a lot, so do not feel sorry for yourself. Focus on what you can do and not what you cannot do.

Adaptation

Time management becomes difficult and you will have less personal time. You will have to figure out what you really want to do and then coordinate with your partner. Having a child will add more responsibilities, whether it was time, cleaning, or finances, you will feel like you barely have time and no control over it. A lot of decisions will be made around the baby's schedule. You will have to get used to it.

To be honest, I tried to do as much reading and learning as I could before Ella was born, but the real lessons began when I first held her in my arms. It is an ongoing process and you learn on the job. So enjoy the small moments, laugh at the mistakes, take it as it comes and you will be okay!

10

EMBRACING THE CHANGE AND THE JOURNEY

Congratulations! You are becoming a father or are already a father to a beautiful child. Your journey with your child will be as special as you choose to make it. You are starting a new chapter in your life. Before I had Ella, I could count the number of times I had held a baby, so the change was daunting. However, Mirabelle and I have turned out to be great parents thanks to the honest communication, support, and love we offer each other. The day I found out Mirabelle was pregnant with Ella; I did everything I possibly could to prepare myself and our home for Ella. I was there for my wife and daughter whenever I had the chance and in retrospect, I am extremely happy with my decisions. Of course, we had a fair share of ups and downs, there were days when I thought I would pull my hair out and there were days when I did not want anything other than my family around me. Is life very different when you become a father? Nearly all men will be concerned that having a child will impact their life. Having a child does not change who you are but it can impact different areas of your life. Some men will view that change as positive, while others may view it in a negative light – the good news is that you get to decide. You are up in the middle of the night because your baby is crying, you could either curse the world and be extremely annoyed or look at your child's face and tell yourself how lucky you. You get to decide how you will approach the situation.

Your journey will be more or less the same, you will be stepping into a new realm and I want to tell you that you will succeed.

Following is a checklist I have prepared for you to tackle all the changes you will be encountering and to prepare you for the pregnancy. You can refer to it anytime you find yourself feeling lost and in need of guidance. Tick off the things you have completed in order to feel you have accomplished something amidst the change you are witnessing. This list can help you prepare everything before your new-born baby arrives in this world;

- Feel and practice gratitude
- Take responsibility for your own emotions
- Get involved with your partner
- Buy minimum necessities for the child
- Improve your financial situation
- Start saving (if you have not already)
- Read, watch videos, attend birthing classes
- Prepare a nursery for your child
- Baby proof the house
- Ask for paternity leave
- Communicate honestly and effectively with your partner
- Build a support system with family and friends
- Find a suitable health plan and birth for the pregnancy
- Help your partner prepare her hospital bag and the baby's hospital bag
- Prepare your own bag
- Take out time for yourself

Good luck on your new journey. I hope you find it in yourself to know that you are already doing a wonderful job at trying to be the best dad you can be – you reading this book is a sign you care.

Thank you for taking out time to read this book I hope it helped you out. Kindly put a review on Amazon.

If you thought it was helpful in any way, I would appreciate it if you could leave a review on Amazon, along with any feedback and suggestions you would have liked to see in the book or other books in the future.

You can mail your feedback and suggestions to: books@alfie-thomas.com

ACKNOWLEDGMENTS

I would not have been able to write this book without the help of my supportive and loving wife, Mirabelle, and my beautiful daughter, Ella, who has taught me so many new things in life. At the center of this book, there are numerous people amongst my family and friends who have helped me along the journey of penning down what it is to be a father, sharing their feedback, being patient with me and always taking interest in my passion to write. I thank you all for being there with me every step of the way. I would not have been able to do it without your support, motivation, and love.

Milton Keynes UK
Ingram Content Group UK Ltd.
UKHW050205120124
435873UK00002B/20